WATCHING FOR THE WIND

*The Seen and Unseen
Influences on Local Weather*

JAMES G. EDINGER has a trait in common with the late Rachel Carson. While tending the apparatus of his science with meticulous discipline, he manages at the same time to keep it from filtering out the human responses to the grandeur he is measuring. Just as Miss Carson turned both a poetic and a scientific eye upon *The Sea Around Us,* so too does Mr. Edinger find aesthetic qualities (as well as differences of pressure and density) in Los Angeles' poisonous smog and in the more benign atmospheric phenomena for which his native California is celebrated.

To chart the currents of air whose movements dictate whether Angelenos will bask in sunshine or hack with coughing has been Mr. Edinger's professional occupation for a quarter of a century. Born in Van Nuys, he attended Pasadena Junior College and the University of California at Los Angeles (A.B., M.A., Ph.D.), where he now is associate professor of meteorology. His father, a teacher of biology and mathematics, gave him an early interest in science; service in the Air Force as weather officer and pilot steered him to meteorology, and environmental science in general. It is perhaps his hours aloft (all intelligent pilots become poets sooner or later) that have given the extra dimension to his writings.

This is Mr. Edinger's first book, but he has contributed to the *Bulletin* and the *Journal of the American Meteorological Society* and the *Journal of Applied Meteorology.*

WATCHING FOR THE WIND
The Seen and Unseen
Influences on Local Weather

James G. Edinger

PUBLISHED BY ANCHOR BOOKS
DOUBLEDAY & COMPANY, INC.
GARDEN CITY, NEW YORK

Watching for the Wind: The Seen and Unseen Influences on Local Weather is published simultaneously in 1967 by Doubleday & Company, Inc.

Anchor Books edition: 1967

ILLUSTRATIONS BY KENNETH E. CROOK

THE SCIENCE STUDY SERIES

This book is one of a number that will appear in the Science Study Series through the collaboration of Educational Services Incorporated and the American Meteorological Society.

The Series was begun, in 1959, as a part of the Physical Science Study Committee's program to create a new physics course for American high schools. The Committee started its work in 1956, at the Massachusetts Institute of Technology, but subsequently became the nucleus of Educational Services Incorporated, of Watertown, Massachusetts, which has carried on the development of new curricula in several fields of education, both in the United States and abroad. The work in physics has had financial support from the National Science Foundation, the Ford Foundation, the Fund for the Advancement of Education, and the Alfred P. Sloan Foundation.

The purpose of the Series is to provide up-to-date, understandable, and authoritative reading in science for secondary school students and the lay public. The list of published and projected volumes covers many aspects of science and technology and also includes history and biography.

The Series is guided by a Board of Editors: Bruce F. Kingsbury, Managing Editor; John H. Durston, General Editor; Paul F. Brandwein of the Conservation Foundation and Harcourt, Brace & World, Inc.; Samuel A. Goudsmit, Brookhaven National Laboratory; Philippe LeCorbeiller, Harvard University; and Gerard Piel, *Scientific American*.

Selected Topics in the Atmospheric Sciences

The American Meteorological Society, with the objectives of disseminating knowledge of meteorology and advancing professional ideals, has sponsored a number of educational programs designed to stimulate interest in the atmospheric sciences. One such program, supported by the National Science Foundation, involves the development of a series of monographs for secondary school students and laymen, and since the intended audiences and the standards of excellence were similar, arrangements were made to include their volumes on meteorology in the Science Study Series.

This series within a series is guided by a Board of Editors consisting of James M. Austin, Massachusetts Institute of Technology; Richard A. Craig, Florida State University; Richard J. Reed, The University of Washington; and Verne N. Rockcastle, Cornell University. The Society solicits manuscripts on various topics in the atmospheric sciences by distinguished scientists and educators.

CONTENTS

WATCHING FOR THE WIND

The Seen and Unseen
Influences on Local Weather

Chapter 1

HOME TOWN WEATHER

This book is written for amateur meteorologists, and, even though you probably don't know it, you qualify as one. Most of your life you have been becoming one; so have all the other people who glance at the sky before going on a picnic or heading for a baseball game. The human race, by and large, is made up of amateur meteorologists. Exceptions to this rule may be the growing number of persons who live in air-conditioned houses and travel to and from air-conditioned offices in air-conditioned cars. But even these more or less hermetically sealed human beings participate in such meteorological activities as adjusting the thermostat on the air conditioner and watching the television weather broadcasts.

You are not, however, a meteorologist in the broad sense of the term. You are a specialist. The sweep of meteorology embraces everything atmospheric from the tiniest drop of dew on a blade of grass to the most terrible storm over the face of the earth. Your area of specialization encompasses only that part of the weather that you can see from the front porch, south forty, or picture window, depending upon your particular station in life. But within these relatively narrow confines, usually a few tens of miles or at most a hundred or so, there is much to behold that is within the province of the meteorologist. He calls it local weather. The chances are pretty good that you and your neighbors know more about your own local weather than does anyone else in the world.

For example, I remember some very good local weather forecasts that my father made while I was a boy. Like you, he was an amateur meteorologist and didn't know it. When on a fall morning he would wake up and see the San Gabriel Mountains a few miles north of our house standing out in exceptionally sharp detail in the early morning sunlight, he would say: "Well, it's going to be a real lolapaloozer today," meaning it was going to be hot as blazes. And it would usually turn out that way. It's likely that you too make some reasonably good forecasts based on that first look at the sky in the morning. But do you know why they are good, or, maybe, why they sometimes aren't?

Unlike you, the professional meteorologists use instruments ranging from microscopes to world-wide networks of weather observatories in making their observations. They also use very complicated electronic devices, radar and artificial earth satellites, for example. They can examine the atmosphere in the minutest detail, or they can stand back and take in the total global picture. Amateurs like you do not have instrumentation to extend your range of observation either to the very small or to the very large. You comprehend only weather on the local scale. For your forecasting you need no special instruments, only a fair set of eyes, a good nose, and your skin with its remarkable ability to detect temperature, humidity, and wind.

Each of us is a walking observatory with at least one big advantage over official observatories. We are mobile. We can move about through the local atmosphere; sense the chill of the air in the lowlands on a clear calm night, then climb to the crest of a hill and delight to the warm balmy breeze above; rock with the gusty winds at the mouth of the canyon on a blustery day, then move over a few hundred yards into the sheltered calm in the lee of a side ridge. Our mobility allows us to detect contrasts over short distances, contrasts that give character, interest, and individuality to the home town or local weather.

No one person can expect to discover all there is to know about local weather or even a small fraction of it. There's simply too much of it. No two towns, no two valleys, no two places regardless of location, have exactly the same local weather. Each has its unique weatherprint. And like the human fingerprint, this weatherprint can be scarred and to some extent modified by the work of man, but not yet, at least, can it be altered beyond recognition. For example, the air immediately downwind of an irrigated field may be deliciously cool and fragrant in contrast to the air that shimmers over the surrounding desert. The sting of the sand and searing heat of the desert wind may be moderated in the lee of a windbreak of tamarisk trees. But the general pattern of the local weather remains unchanged.

The last twenty years have brought many windbreaks, buildings, and alfalfa fields to the desert expanses of the Antelope Valley, just on the other side of the mountains from my home town, but the hot dry westerly wind still sweeps down the length of the valley almost every afternoon. Tumbleweeds roll and bound ahead of the wind just as they have for as long as I can remember. The fences, their west sides plastered with paper, twigs, and all manner of wind-driven trash, give mute evidence of the persistence and direction of this wind. The buildings, the fences, the fields, the irrigation—none of these have changed the cloudless starry nights. The cool quiet dawn still is terminated by the sudden warmth of the red sun rising above the eastern horizon. And although the geometry of cultivated fields is beginning to change the valley's appearance, its brand of local weather stands substantially unaltered by the hand of man. So far only subtle changes in a few details are detectable. Perhaps the most noticeable of these is a slight smudging or blurring of the weatherprint, largely the result of a few millions of people who live outside the valley, in the Los Angeles area some scores of miles upwind. Nowadays, the afternoon wind frequently brings a pale yellowish brown to the southern sky, a highly diluted form of Los Angeles' notorious smog. So you may see some scarring of the local weather if you happen to live in or near a big city. But these changes pale in comparison to the differences in weatherprints that geographical separation fashions. For example, there is the difference between the desert weather of the Antelope Valley and our weather on the other side of the mountains. The variety and contrasts in local weather over the face of the earth are tremendous. As a consequence, no one meteorologist, amateur or professional, can expect to gain an encyclopedic knowledge of it all. In the overwhelming majority of localities the world's expert on local weather will continue to be the fellow in town who has the most observant eye and the most quizzical mind.

In some places the local weather may seem rather dull. Hardly worth writing about. Having been brought up in the Los Angeles area, where the weather provides relatively little excitement in comparison with most parts of the United States, I perhaps was less exposed in boyhood to its fascinations than you were. But now, with the benefit of some formal schooling in the science of the atmosphere, I look back and recollect a childhood generously sprinkled with all manner of interesting and sometimes dramatic weather phenomena.

There were the fires and the floods, the fogs and the freezes. They stand out in the mind's eye as clearly today as they did then, maybe too clearly. For today's fogs, fires, drizzles, and freezes seem much more complicated, more variable from one occasion to the next, than those of my childhood. Each summer does not follow faithfully in the path of the previous one, as I seem to remember it did. I suspect that the local weather as seen through my young eyes took on a becoming, if not somewhat illusory, simplicity. The winters of my childhood were all the same, or so they seemed, a few good rainstorms set against a background of clear sunny weather. When it rained it poured. The gutter along the streets ran full of red brown water, fresh from the foothills of the San Gabriel Mountains. Because the street was so steep the muddy torrent flashed by our house faster than we could walk. My brother and I vowed after each storm that we would build a small boat specially designed to shoot these exciting rapids. But we never did, and I daresay that even the reckless enthusiasm of youth could recognize the formidable problem posed at some cross streets where the turbid waters dived into underground drains.

In those days I paid little attention to rainfall statistics. On the other hand, I remember things like the mud washed up over the doorsills of the houses next to the Sawpit Wash and the missing arches in the long Pacific Electric bridge, washed out by the raging San Gabriel River. On that occasion our eyes saw the steel rails sagging across an awesome gap, a few wooden ties somehow hanging on like the tattered remains of a giant xylophone. Rendering this wild sight all the wilder was the roar of the cataract punctuated with that peculiar hollow thumping made by boulders as they bounded unseen along the rocky bottom. This sort of excitement is denied my children. Flood control dams now check these temper tantrums of the San Gabriel River. Now the scene is quiet, the wash an expanse of bleached granite boulders the year around, the bridge a long array of concrete arches with a small stretch of contrasting steel trusses near the middle, a reminder to the few who remember a different San Gabriel Wash.

I wish I could hear some of the interesting details about the weather in and around your home town. Perhaps about a hurricane if you live on the Gulf Coast, or a tornado if you live in that part of the Midwest referred to (and with good cause) as "tornado alley." If you live along the banks of one of our great rivers you may be able to recount catastrophes that would make my San Gabriel River flood seem picayune. Or if you live in the north it may be a blizzard, something I'll never see in southern California. All such events would to some extent be affected by the physical characteristics of your local area. In studying local meteorology we ask such questions as these: How do hills and valleys affect the wind, the clouds, the fog, the rain, the snow? The local configuration of land, water, vegetation, and building puts its own peculiar stamp on the large-scale weather—be it a blizzard, a flood, or a sunny day, but this imprint of the local terrain is no more than decoration on a bigger weather pattern. We must be able to see this large pattern, just as the cook must have a cake upon which to put the frosting. So let's take a look at the large-scale weather pattern over our hemisphere and find out where that speck called home town sits with respect to the grand design.

Chapter 2

THE IMPRESSIONABLE AIR

Where do you suppose the air that you are inhaling this very moment came from? Where was it yesterday at this time? What about one week ago? As I write this, I can say with some certainty that the cool foggy air outside my window certainly was out over the North Pacific Ocean yesterday, probably far from the sight of land. Chances are good that it has seen nothing but the Pacific Ocean for the last week, although I can't be sure. But right now the air is cool and moist because of where it spent these last few days. And so it is for the air that now surrounds you and your house. Where has it been during the last several days or so? Its itinerary determined whether it is hot or cold, wet or dry. If it is December and the air around you has been moving down across Canada from the arctic wastes, it's cold air. If, on the other hand, your air has been sweeping across the Caribbean this past week before arriving at its present location, it is warm and moist.

Wherever you are and whatever the time of year, the air surrounding you at this moment has not always been the way it is now. You are sensing it at just one moment in its history, a history of ceaseless change. Air is constantly being cooled and heated, moistened and desiccated, tumbled and turned. Last week it may have been baked in the high dry deserts of the Southwest. Two weeks ago it may have been saturated with spray from storm tossed waves of the North Pacific. Three weeks back it may have been refrigerated in Siberia. Or it may have drifted, sultry and suffocating, through a jungle in Southeast Asia.

Our atmosphere is a sponge of sorts. It takes on some of the characteristics of the terrain over which it passes. If it moves quite slowly, lingering for a matter of days, maybe a week, over the same sort of terrain, it comes into equilibrium with that terrain. That is, its temperature and humidity come into harmony with the surface of the earth, whether it be wet or dry, hot or cold. If, on the contrary, the air moves rapidly over the area, it has time to make only small adjustments to the temperature and moisture conditions. The air just hasn't time enough to exchange the available heat and moisture. So if you would know how this air around you got the way it is, you would have to know more than just its itinerary. You would have to know how fast it was driving along each leg of its recent journey over the earth, where the stops were and how long they lasted. And to make things more complicated air has only a limited memory. As it stands now, the air bears mostly the marks of recent experiences. It may have been in the Sahara a month ago, but today it may be as cool and wet as the foggy air outside my window at this moment. In the intervening time it has lost the last vestiges of its condition of thirty days ago. Its most recent adventures are most responsible for its present condition. If we reach back in time far enough, maybe a week, maybe a month, we find that everything that happened previously to this air has been forever erased from its record. So it is that this air of ours moves endlessly over the marvelously rich terrain of the earth. Constantly it is accommodating itself to the changing boundary beneath it. If you would know why weather in your home town has the general character that it has, you must know the favorite paths that the air takes in reaching it. You must know its usual stops along the way. You must know how the road conditions change with the season.

Since we all live in different places our map is going to cover a lot of territory. We will have to treat it in rather large pieces. Let's start with one of the most remarkable stretches of atmospheric highway in the world, the wide flat expanse of central United States and Canada stretching all the way from the Arctic Ocean to the Gulf of Mexico. Over this vast area air may move with equal ease from the north or from the south. (Fig. 1) You have heard perhaps the midwesterner's remark that nothing stood between him and the icebound Arctic but a barbed-wire fence and somebody left the gate open. He might as well have added that he is equally exposed to the south and the hot humid Caribbean. As a direct consequence, the Midwest has some of the most wildly varying weather in the world. Those of you who live there may not realize it, but few other places can claim such marked variability. A day may start out with the temperature in the 60s (Fahrenheit) and within hours see it plummet to well below zero. The air present as the day began may be air that had spent something like a week moving across the warm subtropical Atlantic and Caribbean, finally crossing the Gulf of Mexico before drifting up the broad Mississippi Valley on southerly winds. A sudden shift to northerly winds may bring frigid air in under the warm. This cold air probably has spent a week or two milling around sluggishly, almost motionless, in the Arctic. During this interlude it has taken on the bone-chilling characteristics of its icy environment. When it started moving it probably traveled so rapidly that it didn't have time to come into equilibrium with the warmer surface to the south. So the Midwest gets flooded from the north by a shallow layer of air that shoves the tropical air up above it.

But, you may ask, why the south wind and then the north wind? Why the long stop in the Arctic, the slow trip across the Caribbean? To answer such questions we must consider the pattern of winds. It is particularly important to understand the variability of the pattern. If winds weren't variable, each locality would have the same weather day after day except for the gradual changes that would come with the seasons.

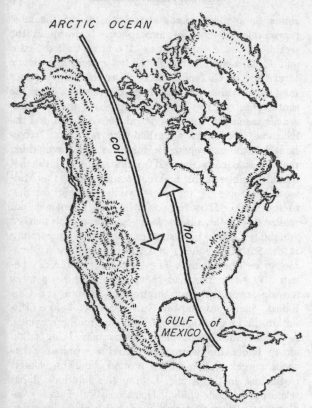

FIG. 1. *Interactions of cold air moving south and hot air moving north along the indicated "atmospheric highway" of our Midwest produce rapid and extreme weather changes.*

The earth's most variable surface winds occur roughly in two broad bands that stretch all around the world, the belts of the westerlies. Each hemisphere, the northern and the southern, has one at about 40 to 55 degrees latitude. The wind patterns equatorward of these two westerly belts show much less day-to-day variation. Hawaii, for example, at 19 degrees north latitude, lies under the most constant winds in the world, the trade winds. Only a few times a year is there any marked change from a northeasterly flow. Then a storm that has drifted rather far from the usual storm tracks temporarily alters things.

The belt of variable winds in the middle latitudes is a broad turbulent air current girdling the globe and flowing from west to east in both the northern and southern hemispheres. If you have seen any of the pictures taken from meteorological satellites you will know why we call the current turbulent. Far from being a simple undisturbed flow from west to east, it is studded with giant whirls and meanderings. It is the passage of these whirls, called cyclones and anticyclones, that bring about the changing winds in the middle latitudes. The cyclones may be 500 to 1000 miles across and move with speeds of 20 or 30 miles per hour. The cyclones normally bring clouds and precipitation. Their winds swirl around in a counterclockwise sense in the northern hemisphere. Curiously enough, the cyclones of the southern hemisphere turn in just the opposite sense. This and many other fascinating features about cyclones are explained in more general books on meteorology.

Most of the United States lies under this turbulent westerly air current, particularly in the winter. The large swirls drift past from west to east. Or sometimes from northwest to southeast or from southwest to northeast. Your home may get winds from any quadrant depending on which side of the cyclone you happen to be at the moment. It may take a day or two for a typical cyclone to pass completely, during which time you may experience one of these dramatic shifts in weather, particularly if you live east of the Rocky Mountains.

If, however, you do not live on such a broad smooth north-south highway you may not see such drastic changes in the temperature with the passing of a cyclone. If you live on the Pacific Coast, for instance, the great stretch of the Rockies stands like a dam 2 or 3 miles high between you and the bitter cold polar air from the Canadian Arctic. But, you may ask, what's to keep the cold Alaskan air from moving down across the nice smooth North Pacific Ocean? Nothing at all. But this air arrives at the coast at temperatures above freezing, not even remotely resembling that sub-zero Canadian air. After all, it has been rubbing up against the ocean for the last thousand miles or so. Even if it had started in the Arctic at sub-zero temperature its journey across the Pacific (which is not frozen) has modified it so that it arrives at the coast with the temperature of the ocean water.

If you live in the Rockies, and that covers a lot of Western territory, you see rather mixed-up weather. Here the rugged terrain distorts the cyclones. Their circulations at the surface can scarcely be distinguished. Local influences to a very large extent determine wind direction. The mountains have an effect on the broad currents of air sweeping around the cyclones and anticyclones similar to that of a rocky cataract on a smoothly flowing river. Smooth flow turns into chaos.

The area is susceptible to both hot and cold air currents. If the cold air from the Canadian Arctic gets deep enough it will be swept over the passes into the interior regions of the Rockies by the northerlies and northeasterlies behind a passing cyclone. But the flow behind the following anticyclone may bring in air all the way from the Caribbean, complete with towering thunderheads and torrential downpours. So the mountainous west sees lots of variable weather too.

We have not mentioned what the anticyclones are. They are giant whirls in the atmosphere rotating in the sense opposite to the cyclones. In contrast to the cyclones, they are fair weather features, frequently cloudless. They provide those sunny episodes between the storms. The usual pattern of flow in the westerlies of the mid-latitudes is a succession of cyclones and anticyclones, one after another. These drift along on the westerly current providing alternate periods of good and bad weather. Cyclones and anticyclones should not be pictured as permanent features. They are constantly forming and dissipating. A typical lifetime might be a week. So we have this churning westerly current in the middle latitudes, full of swirls, some growing, some dying, some great, some small, and all meandering in a generally west to east direction. (Fig. 2)

There are, however, some anticyclones in the world that are very long lived and quite stationary. One of these is responsible for that extremely constant trade wind in Hawaii. It is responsible also for the mild and relatively constant summer weather of coastal California. It stands between California and Hawaii, centered at about 30 degrees north latitude. As a matter of fact, if we could move back and view the globe as a whole we would see that there is a zone circling the earth at about 30 degrees made up of stationary anticyclones. Corresponding to our Pacific subtropical anticyclone there is another in the Atlantic between Africa and Florida. It provides the west coast of North Africa with weather very similar to California's. And it blesses the Caribbean with trades similar to those in Hawaii. And as you might guess, the southern hemisphere also has a globe-girdling zone of anticyclones at about 30 degrees latitude.

So, the southern part of the United States is under the influence of a belt of anticyclones. Florida and the Gulf Coast are usually bathed in the warm humid southeast flow coming around the west end of the Azores anticyclone. The California coast is under the benevolent influence of the cool foggy northwesterlies coming around the east end of the North Pacific subtropical anticyclone. The southwest interior is sort of in between the two. It is left rather high and dry—too far south for most of the storms in the westerlies, too far inland to feel the moderating influences of the oceans. Often, in the summertime, the deep warm moist air from the Caribbean does invade the area, but the trip over the rough dry terrain alters the lower layers beyond recognition. Upstairs, however, the thunderclouds tower, their dark gray bases over a mile above the rough desert terrain. Their brilliant white tops reach

anticyclones

cyclones

Fig. 2. *Though the air in the cyclones and anticyclones rotates, the big whirls themselves tend to drift eastward in middle latitudes (left to right in drawing) across the Pacific and North America. It is this prevailing west-east movement that establishes the grand design of our weather.*

up another six or seven miles into a clean blue sky. From their bases rain comes down in long streamers, which frequently evaporate completely in the arid desert air before wetting the parched earth.

What about the situation poleward of the turbulent westerlies? Most of the time Alaska is being brushed by the very northern extremities of the cyclones. So, it is well exposed to the relatively mild air from the North Pacific. As a matter of fact, the Gulf of Alaska seems to be a favorite target for dying cyclones. Many young cyclones are born where the cold air from Siberia flows out over the relatively warm waters near Japan. These cyclones grow to full size on the drift to mid-Pacific, and by the time the westerlies bring them into the Gulf of Alaska they have just about spent their energy. During much of the year the Gulf is a sort of graveyard for old cyclones. Therefore, the southern coast of Alaska is often under the influence of air with the moderate (by Arctic standards) characteristics of the far North Pacific. The rest of Alaska, like northern Canada, is well exposed to the frigid air of the Arctic.

To fill out our picture of the large-scale features of the weather in the United States we need only superimpose the effect of the seasons, as common sense would suggest. When the days are long and much sunshine is available to heat the earth, the sources of cold air are not so cold, and the sources of warm air are warmer. For the cold season just reverse this effect. Not so obvious, however, is the change in the circulation patterns. The stormy westerlies with their cyclones and anticyclones are found much farther north in summer than in winter. They move north just as the sun does during that season. For example, California gets no rain in the summer because it is south of the seasonal storm tracks in the westerlies. It gets almost all its rain in the winter when the tracks have moved south. Even then so few of them reach southern California that it is classified as a semi-arid region. In the wintertime, however, all the United States (with the possible exception of Hawaii) is fairly vulnerable to the cyclonic storms of the westerlies. Even the southern tip of Florida, Texas, and California can feel the nip of near freezing temperatures every once in a while. In the summer, on the other hand, only the northern states are much affected by cyclones in the westerlies. These cyclones do not then have the extreme cold air in their northerly currents that they do in winter, but their southerly currents bring up the thunderstorms and squall lines for which the Midwest and East are so noted in the summertime. In the late summer and early fall, when the ocean temperatures out in the Equatorial Atlantic are at their highest, over 80 degrees, the trades may bring in the most violent storms of all, the hurricanes (called typhoons in the Pacific). The constant trades give birth to the biggest wind storms of them all. Fortunately, these fearsome storms are not so common as the cyclonic storms of the westerlies. They are confined to one short season and spend most of their lives out over the ocean, away from habitation.

So, the sum total of the weather in your home town, no matter where it is, depends to a considerable extent on large-scale features in the atmospheric circulations. These circulations prescribe the history of the air that reaches you. They determine the sequence of heating and cooling, moistening and desiccation to which the air is subjected as it travels its varied path to your door. Your local environment is just the latest in an unending series of modifiers that put their stamps on the air. Its imprint is newest, therefore is clearest. Add it to the characteristics already fashioned by the previous history and you form the sum, the atmosphere you see and feel about you right now.

Next we must find out how local terrain acts as weather maker, or at least as weather modifier. In the following chapter we examine the physical processes that can alter the lowest layer of the atmosphere and the weather that it fashions.

Chapter 3

AIR AND WATER

When you go to the window and see some sort of
weather, chances are you're looking at just water.
For example, a big thunderhead (cumulonimbus
cloud), that manufacturer of thunder, lightning, and
tree-snapping winds, is just water. The glistening bulk
of the cloud that looks for all the world like a giant
cauliflower is really a vast collection of very small water
droplets, each only a few hundredths of an inch in
diameter. The individual droplet is much too small to
be seen with the unaided eye, but the aggregation,
packed hundreds in each cubic inch of the cloud, when
seen at a distance present an appearance as substantial
and brilliant as polished marble. The fuzzed-out upper
portion of the cloud, spreading in the typical anvil
shape, is also water, in its solid form, tiny ice crystals,
also much too small to be seen individually. And the
stuff slanting out of the ominous gray bottom of the
cloud is water, maybe in the form of snowflakes (a
bunch of ice crystals stuck together) or as raindrops
(water drops maybe a million times larger by volume
than the tiny cloud droplets). So associated with this
one particular type of cloud we have water in a great
variety of forms: raindrops, snowflakes, cloud droplets,
and ice crystals.

Most all the weather we see is water in one of these
forms. Most of the clear weather you "see" is clear only
because water in yet another form is quite invisible.

This phase, of course, is water in its gaseous form, water vapor. Typically we are surrounded by water, invisible gaseous water. Were it visible we would be able to see nothing else. We'd be like fish in a turbid sea, unable to see anything but our gaseous environment. Fortunately, it is only when water occurs in its liquid or solid form that it can obstruct our vision. But we can *feel* water vapor, in a sense, at least. We are aware of it when it occurs in such high concentrations that our perspiration does not evaporate readily and we get that "sticky" feeling. Conversely, we are aware of its absence, or near absence, when the water vapor content of the air is low and our skin gets dry and our lips become chapped.

Most of the things we call weather, then, are formed when, for one of a number of reasons, this ever-present invisible form of water changes into visible water. Now, if this were a book about cloud physics* we could go into some interesting but intricate explanations of why cloud droplets form in the atmosphere and why it rains, snows, hails, and sleets. Here we will be interested primarily in discovering only the most important factors that determine where and when clouds with or without rain and snow are likely to appear (and disappear) in the local environment.

Why does water vapor change to liquid water? If we tried to answer the question conscientiously we soon would be too far afield. So let's be satisfied with finding out when (meaning in what circumstances) water vapor condenses to form droplets and crystals. If you liked, you could take the air between you and this printed page and cause some of its water vapor to condense. All you would have to do would be to cool it down to its dew point temperature. At that temperature the air will be saturated. It will contain as much water vapor as it can. Any further cooling will cause

* See *Cloud Physics and Cloud Seeding* by Louis J. Battan (Science Study Series S29).

some of its water vapor to condense out in one form or other. If it's a humid day (high water vapor content) it won't take much cooling, a few degrees maybe, to turn the trick. On a drier day it would take considerably more. Breathe into the freezer. You'll make a lot of tiny water droplets, a miniature fog. If it's cold enough outside the house, you won't be able to avoid making clouds of your own every time you exhale. So, one way, and by all odds the most frequent way, clouds form in the atmosphere is simply by cooling. Cooling can quickly change the invisible but vapor-laden atmosphere into an opaque cloud.

If we would find out about cloud formation we must find out how cooling occurs in the atmosphere. At the ground it's easy. The air can rub up against something cold and be chilled (lose some of its heat to the cold object by the process we call conduction). A good example is San Francisco's fog. The dull gray mist that streams through the Golden Gate is air that has been sliding over a narrow band of cold water which wells up from the oceanic depths along the northern California coastline. The air has lost heat to the cold ocean water and becomes sufficiently chilled to condense out some of the water vapor in the form of fog droplets (the same as cloud droplets). But what about the clouds that form high above the earth's surface, up where there is nothing cold to rub against except more air? Obviously there must be other ways in which air can lose heat.

Radiation is one such process. Now, your experience may suggest that radiation always warms you—never cools you. Let me remind you that you are not only an absorber of radiant heat; you, like the sun, are a radiator of heat as well. The radiant energy that makes the long trip from the sun across nearly empty space originated in the atoms that collectively make up the sun. When the electrons jiggle about in these atoms they produce electromagnetic waves that move out in space in all directions. This wave phenomenon is what we call radiant energy. You too are made up of atoms, and your atoms have electrons. These electrons also jiggle and give off radiation. You may protest that you, unlike the sun, do not glow. Not all radiation is visible. Sir William Herschel made this discovery in 1799. Using a prism to spread the visible light from the sun out into a spectrum, he placed a thermometer in the various colors to see which one would transmit the most heat to the thermometer. In the course of the experiments, he once left his thermometer in the darkness just beyond the red end of the spectrum. To his astonishment he found that the temperature there rose too. Some invisible radiation from the sun, what we now call infrared radiation, was transferring heat.

You and I are also infrared radiators. In fact, everything in the world is a radiator of heat energy. There is a simple relation that tells why the sun is a more powerful radiator than you are. It says that the energy radiated is proportional to the fourth power of the absolute temperature of the radiator. This law tells us that if we increase the absolute temperature of an object by a factor of two, the rate at which it radiates energy will increase by $2 \times 2 \times 2 \times 2$ (2 to the fourth power) which is 16. The sun, whose temperature is roughly 20 times that of the earth (or you, for that matter) therefore radiates $20 \times 20 \times 20 \times 20$, which equals 160,000 times more energy from each square foot of its surface than you do or a similar area on the earth does. But the equation also tells us that even liquid helium at only 2 degrees above absolute zero radiates some heat—not much, but some. So when you open the refrigerator door its inside walls radiate some heat out at you, strange as that may seem! And you absorb this radiant energy. The only reason you don't warm up as a consequence is that you are making a bad bargain. You, at your higher temperature, are radiating (losing) more heat to the refrigerator than it is radiating (giving back) to you. Now, the thin atmosphere also is a radiator and absorber and obeys radiation laws. At night it can be cooled by losing more radiant energy to the cold earth and space than it receives back from these two sources. During the day, of course, the sun gets into the act and the situation is considerably altered in favor of atmospheric heating.

Up to now we have at our disposal two ways in which air can be cooled, conduction and radiation. Both of these are relatively slow processes in the atmosphere. Conduction is slow because air is a notoriously poor conductor of heat. If it were not we could never get close enough to a lighted stove to turn off the burners. Changes in air temperature due to radiative exchange are found to be of the order of only a degree a day in that part of the atmosphere where we get clouds and weather. It can be as much as about a degree per hour at ground levels. We must find some other and faster cooling process if we are to explain the rapid cooling that we know to occur well above the ground in most cloud building situations. This other process is not an obvious one. It is, however, the most important one by far, accounting for most of what we call weather. It is the simple process of lifting air. Lift air and you cool air. Incredible? Not really. Just consider the following simple experiment.

Fill a rubber balloon with air at the ground. Also fill a metal sphere with air. Note the temperature of the air. Now we lift both containers up to a level 100 meters (328 feet) above the ground, being careful that no heat is transferred to the air samples by conduction or radiation or any other process. We measure the temperature of the air in the metal sphere and find that it hasn't changed. Maybe lifting air doesn't cool it after all! But wait. Let's check the temperature of the air in the balloon. It has cooled by one degree Centigrade (1.8 degrees Fahrenheit). Why should the two samples of air behave differently? There is a difference between the two containers. The balloon, being elastic, actually increased in size while being lifted. Although the change in volume was much too small (about one quarter of one percent) to be detected by eye, the air in the balloon did expand, just as free air would have expanded, while the air in the rigid sphere was constrained to remain at constant volume. So, that one degree of cooling was the result of expansion of the air.

Now, the idea of cooling gas by expansion has a familiar ring to it because some ordinary things we do involve the expansion and contraction of air. For example, have you ever noticed how cool the air feels that comes out of a bicycle or automobile tire? This is a simple case of air expanding upon being released from the inside of the tire where it had been confined at high pressure in a small volume. Conversely, of course, the air gets hot in the process of being squeezed back into the tire. Feel the tire pump after you fill the tire and you'll see how warm it got. Other common examples include venting compressed carbon dioxide from a storage cylinder. The compressed gas in the cylinder, at something like room temperature and a pressure of 2000 pounds per square inch (considerably higher than tire pressures), suddenly expands into the atmosphere, where the pressure is only about 15 pounds per square inch. The volume increases by a factor of 100 or better, and the carbon dioxide cools off enough (below -78 degrees Centigrade) to freeze in the form of dry ice; it leaves the nozzle as a powdery white spray. So, if you would like to cool air in a hurry, all you need do is to expand it in a hurry. From our experiment with the balloon we can conclude that free air expands when it rises in the atmosphere. Rapidly rising air is rapidly cooling air, and air that may soon become visible as a cloud of some sort.

But we haven't explained why air lifted in the atmosphere expands. The explanation seems simple enough. Atmospheric pressure is greatest at the ground and steadily decreases up through the atmosphere. A balloon as it rises is subjected to less and less squeezing by the surrounding atmosphere. Consequently the air expands. But, as with so many answers, this one leads to another more basic question: why does atmospheric pressure decrease with elevation? I think the question is better put just the other way around. Why does atmospheric pressure increase as we descend? Let's jump into the swimming pool and find out.

Take a deep breath and head for the bottom. The deeper you go the more water there is above you and this greater weight of water pushes in on you and tends to compress you. You can feel it, especially on your eardrums. Being made of relatively incompressible materials, liquids and solids, your volume doesn't change much, but if you were gaseous, like the air in our balloon, you would become smaller. Now come up for air. The pressure lessens regularly and finally vanishes as you leave the pool. But what you may not realize is that here, outside the pool, you are still being squeezed, now by atmospheric pressure, to which we are all so accustomed that we are completely unaware of it. As you sit at the edge of the pool, you are actually sitting at the bottom of an ocean of air. This ocean of air has weight equivalent to that of an ocean of water 32 feet deep. Pressure increases downward in this ocean of air for the same reason that it increased downward in the swimming pool. In both cases lower layers must bear the total weight of all upper layers, and a pressure, just commensurate to the task, is developed. When we "swim" (by aircraft) up into our ocean of air pressures should decrease. At 18,000 feet above sea level we will have left below us about half of the weight of the atmosphere. Consequently, the air above will be squeezing in on us with only half the force that the total atmosphere exerted at the surface. If we had brought our balloon along it would have almost doubled in volume. On the other hand, if we had taken a balloon full of air down 32 feet below the surface of a lake, say, it would have shrunk to about half its original volume.

People who dive to considerable depths beneath the water have to worry about such pressure and volume changes, as do pilots who fly (without pressurized suits or cabins) to high elevations. If proper precautions are not observed the effects can be fatal. It would be out of place here to enumerate the many kinds of physical damage that can result when the body is exposed to unusual pressures, large or small, but let me dramatize a little the relation between pressure and volume in a gas by recounting an experience I had the first time I made an ocean dive with SCUBA gear. SCUBA stands for *self contained underwater breathing apparatus*. All it requires is a cylinder of compressed air with a pressure-regulated breathing line that serves as a supply of air for the swimmer. It's a marvelous device for freeing yourself from a dependence on the atmosphere while exploring the underwater world.

When you are swimming below the surface, the pressure regulator on the tank allows you to breathe in air that is at the same pressure as the water at that level. At 32 feet down you are inhaling air that is at twice atmospheric pressure. As you swim up toward the surface you breathe in air that is progressively at lower pressures until just at the surface you are breathing air at atmospheric pressure. Now contrast that with the situation if you dived without SCUBA gear. After taking a good deep breath at the surface you would descend to 32 feet. There the doubled pressure would have squeezed in on you enough to have decreased by one half the volume of your lungs. The same air would be occupying only half the space it did when you inhaled it, but it would be at about twice the pressure and twice the density (mass per unit volume or, say, pounds per cubic foot). If you held your breath all this time and rose to the surface your lungs would expand on the way up until, at the surface, they would be back to normal size again.

Well, on this occasion I did have SCUBA gear and didn't have to go through such a breath-holding ordeal. We were swimming in a sea garden at about 30 feet below the surface off Santa Cruz Island, in southern California. It was my first ocean dive in such beautiful surroundings, and I was thrilled beyond my powers of description with a new and strange world. New shapes, new colors, new lights, and most of all, this new magical ability to float around in my environment. We all dream of being able to float around in the air, leaping from mountain peak to mountain peak, gliding suspended above a valley. This glorious freedom is possible underwater. The utterly unattainable attained, the impossible an accomplished fact.

We glided about through forests of giant kelp, coasting effortlessly, turning this way and that. Occasionally we swam down to inspect bits of gaudy vegetation on the sea floor or an abalone or a big sculpin. We would take out after some brightly colored fish to see how close we could get to him. How much time we spent in this happy exploring I don't really remember, but suddenly the air wasn't coming out of the tank easily. I had to suck a little harder to get air. My tank was empty. No matter—this problem is easily solved. There was plenty of air just 30 feet above me. So up I went.

I remembered to exhale all the way, making bubbles as I rose, and it was a very comfortable and safe ascent. I arrived at the surface with my lungs still comfortably full of air. Why wasn't I all out of air? You probably have guessed. Down at 30 or 35 feet, because of the doubled pressure, my lungs had twice as much air in them as they normally do above water. On the way up I exhaled what at normal atmospheric pressure would have been a full chest of air, but since I started out below with twice that much, I arrived at the top with lungs still full. No empty, breathless sensation at any time, just that remarkably relaxed feeling of being able to exhale endlessly without cramp or collapse of the chest.

But what if I had ignored or forgotten those important instructions that are drilled into beginners with SCUBA gear, and had held my breath on the way up? I would have arrived at the surface with the pressure inside my lungs double the atmospheric pressure outside my body. Lung tissues, like the skin of an overinflated balloon, would have been stressed to the breaking point. A serious, sometimes fatal, chain of events culminating in air bubbles in the blood stream would have resulted—an air embolism. I would have learned the hard way (and too late) the important relationship of pressure, density, and the volume of a gas.

Returning then to meteorology, we see that a few notions about the physics of the atmosphere provide us with a simple rule: lift air and it will expand and in expanding, cool; let air sink and it will be compressed and become heated. All we need do now is to find out what makes air go up and down and we will have the explanation why most clouds form where they do and when they do. Mostly, if viewed on the global scale, air goes back and forth horizontally. Its ups and downs are but side excursions on the vast horizontal circulation. There are ripples as well as boiling and bubbling here and there, but these movements only give texture to the broad sweeping currents of air sliding over the surface of our globe. Pictures taken from satellites show this distinction quite dramatically. Of course, what on the global scale seems no more than a little bubbling and boiling can on the local scale take on the aspect of uncontrolled fury. Bulging monsters of clouds, thunder, lightning, torrential rain—nature on the rampage. And this awesome spectacle largely results from the lifting of air a few miles up into the atmosphere. Most clouds require far less lifting. Those global ripples that to us down here on earth look like broad white bands of clouds stretching from one horizon to the other probably require a lift of only a small fraction of a mile. It is plain, then, that our atmosphere with its water vapor is very sensitive to vertical motion.

If we but understood the hows and whys of vertical motions in the atmosphere we would be well on our way to understanding cloud formation and dissipation. There are several ways in which vertical motion can be generated in the atmosphere. They are distinctive, each bringing about different sorts of weather and cloud forms. Perhaps the most obvious is the lifting that occurs when horizontally moving air encounters an obstacle such as a mountain range and is forced up the slope. You may have noticed that mountains get more than their fair share of clouds and precipitation. This is one of the reasons. Lots of the ripples, large and small scale, that occur in the atmosphere are the result of the forcing of the atmosphere up and down over mountainous terrain. The outcome is not unlike the waves and ripples formed on water as it flows over a rocky stream bed. These atmospheric ripples form very distinctive types of clouds that differ in some very interesting ways from other clouds. We will discuss them in some detail in a later chapter.

Another way in which air is forced upward is by what we call horizontal convergence, a fancy name for crowding air into a smaller horizontal area. The obvious result is that the air, like toothpaste in a tube, is forced to move upward at right angles to the squeeze. But what in the world would squeeze air? Of course, it has to be the air itself. A good example is to be found in the converging sea breezes of the Florida peninsula. The daytime winds blowing from the sea and the Gulf toward the peninsula—one across the eastern coastline the other across the western—obviously converge. The air has to go somewhere. It can't go into the ground so it goes up. This upward motion has something to do with setting off Florida's summer thunderstorms although it is by no means the whole story.

Horizontal convergence can be generated in other ways not associated with terrain features. It is inherent in some types of horizontal motion. For example, as mentioned in the previous chapter, the atmosphere frequently organizes itself in the form of large whirls, many hundreds of miles across, called cyclones and anticyclones. Typically the air either spirals in (converges) or spirals out (diverges) of these areas, giving rise to either upward or downward motion of the air. We must be careful, however, in deciding which is cause and which is effect. Sometimes the air is being forced to rise by some other mechanism and the surrounding air moves in (converges) as a consequence. The last means for lifting air that we will discuss is just such a mechanism, a force that directly pushes upward or downward on the air. This force is called buoyancy. It is the force that propels a cork upward in water. The important thing is that this same force can also propel water upward through water and air upward through air.

Buoyancy is really quite simple. You need only recall that pressures in liquids and gases increase as you go from top to bottom. If you put a rock under water, less pressure will be exerted downward on the top of the rock than is exerted upward on the bottom of the rock. The result is a net upward pressure force on the rock as a whole. Then why doesn't the rock rise as a cork does in water? Another force, gravity, is acting in the opposite direction, downward. Objects rise or fall in a fluid environment depending upon whether pressure or gravity wins the vertical tug-of-war. We have a special name for the resultant vertical force (the difference between the upward pressure force and the downward gravity force). We call it buoyancy.

As you know, the force exerted by gravity on an object depends upon the mass of the object. In the case of the cork in water, gravity is the weaker of the two forces, and so the buoyancy is directed upward. We call this positive buoyancy. In the case of the rock in water, gravity is the stronger of the two forces, and the buoyancy is directed downward. This we call negative buoyancy.

For fun (and maybe for a little better insight into buoyancy) let's try to think of cases in which there is a dead heat between the two forces—in other words, when buoyancy is zero. A goldfish remaining motionless in a fish bowl is a good example. As a matter of fact, so are you when you exhale just enough air to float motionless beneath the surface of the swimming pool.

The most instructive example of all is water in water. Consider that cubic foot of water down there, right in the middle of the swimming pool, say halfway between the top and the bottom. It is motionless, going neither up nor down. Its buoyancy must be zero. Now isn't it miraculous that the force of gravity on that cubic foot of water should so perfectly balance the net upward pressure force on it? No, not at all. Remember, it is gravity pulling down on the fluid environment above the cube of water that produces the pressure forces in the first place. And the all-important increase in pressure as we move from the top of the cube one foot down to the bottom of the cube is due to gravity pulling down on that intervening one foot of water.

So, if we replace that cubic foot of water with something denser than water (weighing more per cubic foot), that something is going to "fall like a rock." Conversely, if we replace it with something that is less dense than water that something is going to "bob up like a cork." Of course, the environmental fluid need not be water. It could be any liquid or gas. It could be air. Yes, there is a net upward force pushing you away from the earth. And were it not for the fact that you are denser than air you'd be taking off over the treetops or banging your head on the ceiling. (It happens all the time to balloons filled with helium.) The rule is simple. Things that are less dense than the fluid in which they are immersed are subject to a positive (upward) buoyancy force. Those that are denser are subject to a negative (downward) buoyancy force. (Fig. 3)

You are aware that meteorologists use balloons in their work. Usually the balloons are vehicles for carrying instruments like thermometers up into the atmosphere. They are filled with a light gas, hydrogen or helium, to make them positively buoyant. There are times, however, when special nonexpandable balloons are inflated with a mixture of air and helium to keep them floating at one particular level in the atmosphere. If pushed up above that level they become negatively buoyant in the less dense air aloft and sink back to their floating level. If pushed down they become positively buoyant in the denser air below and rise back up to that level. Such balloons provide an excellent method for tagging a piece of air and seeing

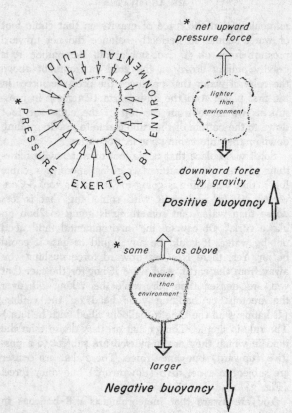

FIG. 3. *The sum of the environmental forces acting up and down on a given volume of air determines whether it has positive buoyancy (rises) or negative buoyancy (descends). In the illustration the relative magnitudes of the opposing forces are indicated by the relative lengths of the arrows. Thus, the upper parcel of air is rising because the net force upward is greater than the downward pull of gravity. Air movements under these buoyancy forces cause local vertical currents.*

how and where it moves. They are released and then tracked by means of special devices, such as radar.

A few years ago mylar balloons specially designed for this sort of tracking were used in Los Angeles in a study of the movement of polluted air. To make them easily "seen" by radar, they had a thin (one molecule thick) coating of aluminum. They were tetrahedral in shape, like a pyramid. To the spectator on the ground, one of these balloons no doubt presented a startling spectacle, a shiny metallic pyramid about four feet on a side floating overhead, an unidentified flying object if ever there was one.

We had the assignment of circling these balloons in an instrumented light aircraft as they floated above Los Angeles, to make measurements of temperature, humidity, and elevation in their vicinity. The first test proceeded beautifully for several hours as one of the balloons moved with the air right across the city. But when it reached the east side of town it was carried to fairly low elevation in a large area of downdrafts, and for safety we in the plane had to observe it from above. Shortly we noticed a helicopter approaching the balloon below us, and we could scarcely believe our eyes as the copter maneuvered about trying to blow the balloon down to the ground in the downdraft under the whirling rotor blades. The balloon, forced so far beneath its floating level, was very buoyant in the positive sense, and the helicopter pilot soon found that the mysterious metallic pyramid had a mind of its own. No sooner would he get it blown down close to the ground than it would bob crazily up again.

About this time we noticed some police cars parked in a vacant lot. A group of policemen were running about leaping for the balloon whenever it came close to the ground, like basketball players going for a rebound. Their spirited game involving our sophisticated apparatus went on for some time, perhaps to their amusement but certainly not to ours. It is only now, with the passage of time, that I can appreciate the humor. At

the moment we were incensed to see our most successful tracking experiment, in jeopardy from their ridicu-
lous cavortings—grown men, guardians of the law,
protecting the community from a balloon!

Then it happened. The copter got too close and . . .
one metallized balloon in a million pieces. There wasn't
enough left of our unidentified flying object to identify.
What had happened, obviously, was that many persons
had called the police about the strange (and sinister!)
object, despite the fact that newspaper descriptions of
the experiments had been published in advance. The
police had dispatched the helicopter to round up the
mysterious intruder and force it down for capture. Positive buoyancy defeated them.

So, by way of an absurd incident we return to the
subject, how can air by made buoyant? All we must
do is change the density of the air in question with respect to its air environment. But how is this done? Simply by heating or cooling it. When air is heated it expands. In other words, it becomes less dense, has
less mass in a cubic foot. When it is cooled it contracts
and becomes more dense. Thus, we have another source
of vertical motion in the atmosphere, heat. Heat produces "atmospheric corks," masses of air that are warmer
and therefore less dense than the surrounding atmosphere. You've seen some of these atmospheric corks,
but only after they have risen high enough and cooled
enough by expansion to form liquid droplets. They
are, of course, the familiar cumulus clouds, their tops
rounded off in the process of being pushed forcibly up
through the denser environment.

Now we have a few simple tools at hand. We are
ready to move out into the local atmosphere and explore. Since we must discover the places where and
the times when vertical motions occur locally, and since
these up and downdrafts often depend upon the horizontal air motion (wind), let's begin by learning about
local winds.

Chapter 4

SEEING THE WIND

In setting about to explore the local atmosphere for
the patterns of air motion we are immediately faced
with a rather substantial problem: how do you see
something that normally is invisible? Well, you don't
see it, but ordinarily you can see something that is being affected by it—the fluttering leaves on a tree, a scrap
of paper bounding along the ground, the spindrift from
a cresting wave. If the wind is strong enough you will
feel it. It may even snatch the hat off your head. However, if it is less than one or two miles per hour you
won't be able to feel it unless you can specially sen-
sitize yourself. Moisten a finger and hold it up. It will
feel cooler on its upwind side, due to increased evaporation there. Or do as the marksman does before he
takes aim. Toss a little dust in the air. But whatever
methods you use, you normally get only spot checks on
the wind in space and time. Ideally, we would like to
know the flow at every point continuously—in other
words, the complete pattern, no holes allowed.

Since the entire pattern is beyond our capabilities,
we must do the best we can. Look about you at this instant, for example, and see how many wind indicators
you can spot—trees, flags, loose debris, smoke, dust,
anything that gives an indication of air motion. For
each of these points you have some idea of the wind.
Do all the indicators report the same wind? Probably
not. Keep watching and I think you'll detect dif-

ferences—not only from one point to another but also from one instant to the next. You've probably noticed that the flag often moves erratically from one side of the pole to the other. You've seen the tree bend under the force of a gust, then straighten up only to bend again in a somewhat different direction. And when one tree is whipping and bobbing, another tree a block away may be standing almost undisturbed. Now contemplate all that empty space between your odd collection of wind indicators. It must be the site of who knows what elaborate air flow patterns, patterns that come and go, unseen, unappreciated. How little we really know about the small scale structure of air flow!

In some unusual cases we are able to see a fairly detailed picture of the flow near the ground. If the wind gets strong enough, things normally unaffected by gentle winds suddenly, like your hat, become good wind indicators. How completely the flying debris defines the terrible vortex of the tornado! Or the blowing sand the swirling column of the dust devil. In some cases nature provides very closely spaced wind indicators on land, such as the individual stalks of wheat in a grain field. Spotted here and there about the fields we have the usual indicators, perhaps a windmill, a tree here and there, maybe even some washing billowing on the clothesline. They may tell us there is a strong gusty wind from the west. How much more eloquent and detailed is the tale the waves across that golden ocean of grain tell. The wind comes in waves across the fields— and not like the well-ordered swell of the open ocean. At any moment the field has a more tousled appearance and each tousled blond wave moves across the field as if yielding to an invisible brush of heroic dimensions.

The amateur usually must put up with a frustratingly incomplete picture of the pattern of air flow. What do you suppose the professional meteorologist does about detecting the continuous pattern of air flow? At the local scale he is as handicapped as you are, at least in most instances. He's just another wind watcher. He can't afford to put up an anemometer and wind vane every 10 feet or every 100 feet or even every 1000 feet. But at the larger, nationwide scale he does have available to him the wind reports from a network of hundreds of stations established by the government. These are the data you see on a regular weather map. The spacing between the stations is normally something like 50 miles, and from their data he is able to interpolate a continuous field of flow that approximates the actual large-scale flow. At this scale the cyclones and anticyclones are clearly revealed by the analysis. But you see no local wind patterns on the map. All this sort of map can reveal are features that are large compared to the 50-mile distance between stations. But while you cannot see the small local patterns, you can detect their influence. You have but to look at the chaos in the western (mountainous) part of the United States. Here the local effects are so great that they almost completely obscure the large-scale flow. Wind reports from adjacent stations in this part of the country characteristically bear little resemblance to each other. In the relatively smooth eastern part of the country, however, local effects disturb a wind only here and there, leaving the general pattern of the cyclone or anticyclone easily distinguishable. Consequently, in locating wind instruments for detecting the large-scale pattern the meteorologist takes great care to find spots where local effects are minimum—remote from buildings, trees, and rugged terrain. In mountainous areas he finds these ideal locations almost nonexistent.

In some special circumstances the meteorologist does space the wind-measuring equipment close enough together to discover the local flow pattern. This coverage is so expensive, however, that the justification must be quite compelling. Los Angeles smog with its associated problems is that compelling. So, more than fifty extra wind stations have been installed in the city. Stations in the area are spaced at intervals of 5 or 10 miles. Analyses of data from this dense network of wind stations show clearly the local wind patterns. So rich is the Los Angeles region in terrain features that the large-scale wind field is practically undetectable. In the absence of local effects the wind usually would be from the northwest, as furnished by the subtropical anticyclone between Hawaii and California. Instead, the general flow across the area is at right angles to this direction. The flow is twisted and tortured by the hills, valleys, mountains, and canyons. A later chapter will examine the relationship between these local winds and smog.

Sometimes the meteorologist is required to obtain wind data on an even smaller scale. Such places as large rocket-launching sites and atomic energy plants require a very detailed knowledge of the local winds. Rapid changes in wind direction and strength can threaten the stability of devices during the critical launch period. They also specify the subsequent transport and dispersal of dangerous materials loosed into the atmosphere, exotic rocket fuels and radioactive materials.

In some instances measurements of the wind have even been made at distances of the order of only a foot or so. We once constructed wind maps based on data this closely spaced. The maps represented the horizontal wind field at 1000 feet above the ground for an area 150 feet long and 50 feet wide. They revealed what looked like small cyclones and anticyclones, patterns not unlike those we see on citywide and nation-wide maps. In this case our wind indicators were soap bubbles released from a bubble generator suspended below a large captive balloon. Their motions were photographically determined with a special motion picture camera.

What do you suppose we would find if we were to make maps based on wind observations spaced only an inch apart? It has been done in the laboratory by photographing the minute motions of little bits of lint. You have probably seen small motes moving through a thin shaft of sunlight in a dark room. They have an almost star-like brilliance against the dark background. Barns are usually good places in which to see the effect. There are lots of small cracks through which the sun can throw a shaft of light and there is an abundant supply of small bits of fiber and dust floating in the air. The air motions that these illuminated motes reveal are just as elaborate as those seen on wind maps at the other three scales. What a remarkable living tapestry the atmosphere must be! It is just as patterned when seen at a distance of 5 inches as it is when seen from 500 miles out in space. What a pity we can't really see it.

Chapter 5

TERRAIN, SCULPTOR OF THE WIND

If the global winds do not produce the elaborate local scale air motions, then what are the influences that do? Actually, there are quite a few processes capable of fashioning local winds. They can be separated conveniently into two camps: (a) those that take the winds provided to the local area by the large-scale flow and turn them into new paths and (b) those that start from scratch, with no wind at all, and manufacture a local breeze. In this chapter we will discuss the first of these groups, the processes that take the wind as delivered and distort it.

Has it occurred to you that the air has a choice when it encounters an isolated hill? It can go either over the hill or around it. Usually, but by no means always, its flow about the hill is some sort of combination of going around and going over. And the same is true of a low pass through a mountain range. On some days the air moving against the upwind slopes of a mountain range is squeezed through the pass with gale force. On other days the air almost as easily passes right up over the mountain range. On the one hand the air apparently resists going uphill and on the other finds such vertical displacement quite to its liking. The basic question seems to be: why does it take more force to push air uphill on one day than it does on another? A large part of the answer has to do with the buoyancy forces that we have discussed. Let's examine how they influence air being displaced vertically.

To keep things as simple as possible, let's assume that the air forced up the mountain slope is not heated or cooled by the mountain itself. Let's fix our attention on the two packets of air involved—the air being lifted up the slopes and the unlifted air going around the mountain. It is a fact that even in this simple case the lifted air may take on a different temperature from the unlifted air at the same elevation, sometimes colder, sometimes warmer. What sort of funny business is this? As you can imagine, it is rather important business because when the slope air is warmer than its environment it is positively buoyant. It no longer requires any pushing to make it go uphill. Its own buoyancy insists that it do so. Conversely, when the slope air is cooler than its environment as a result of being pushed upslope it is negatively buoyant. If no stronger force is available to push it farther up the mountain the air will slide right back down the hill. Our task is clear. If we are to understand why on some occasions the air resists being pushed up the mountain and on others it doesn't, we must find out why it sometimes becomes colder than its environment and why sometimes it gets warmer—even when it is not being cooled or heated by the mountain.

There is a simple experiment that will simulate our problem. Let's represent the lifted air by a balloon full of air at the ground. With a thermometer hung inside the balloon we can monitor the internal temperature as the balloon is lifted. We also hang a thermometer outside the balloon to give us readings at all times of the temperature of the environmental (unlifted) air around the balloon. In this way we will be able to determine whether our balloon becomes buoyant. The two thermometers show the same temperature at the ground because we fill the balloon with air taken from the environment there. We now lift the balloon and thermometers up to 100 meters above ground, taking all necessary precautions against any transfer of heat between the air in the balloon and its environment. As you recall from previous discussions, the balloon will have expanded, and as a result the temperature of the air in the balloon will have decreased by one degree C. Without looking at the two thermometers what would you guess is the difference in temperature between the air in the balloon and the air outside here at 100 meters? Now be careful! It's tempting to conclude that it will be one degree colder inside the balloon. But (and here's the catch) the air outside the balloon up here at 100 meters may have a different temperature from that of the air at the ground. You probably have noticed that air usually is colder at high elevations. In fact, it usually is, though not always.

Meteorologists have been sending instruments up on kites, balloons, and airplanes for years. Data obtained in this way have established that the air aloft is usually (not always) cooler than the air below it in the lowest few miles of the atmosphere. They call the rate of this decrease in temperature with increasing height the temperature lapse rate. A typical value for the lapse rate in the lower atmosphere is ⅔ degree C per 100 meters. This means that a bird 100 meters above your head is flying in air ⅔ degree cooler than the air in which you are standing. Suppose that when we did our experiment the atmosphere had this typical temperature stratification. Then the thermometer on the outside of the balloon would have detected a ⅔ degree C decrease at the same time that the air in the balloon had been cooling by one degree C by expansion. Result: the balloon at 100 meters is ⅓ degree cooler than its new environment. So it is negatively buoyant and opposes being pushed up any higher. Indeed, it will fall right back to the ground if it is not supported.

But the thermal stratification of the atmosphere is not always ⅔ degree C per 100 meters. There is a large variation about this figure from place to place and from time to time. For example, there is a large fluctuation in the lapse rate in the lowest few thousand feet of the atmosphere from day to night, even from morning to afternoon. Let's suppose we conducted our experiment when the lapse rate was exactly one degree C per 100 meters, not an unlikely value for the middle of a sunny day over most land areas. The thermometer in the balloon would again, as always, show a one degree cooling by expansion upon being lifted 100 meters. But in an atmosphere having this special stratification, the thermometer on the outside of the balloon will show that the surrounding air at 100 meters also is just one degree C cooler than the air at the ground. Result: no temperature difference inside and outside, zero buoyancy force. In this case it's just as easy to push the air uphill as it is to push it horizontally.

One last experimental run and we'll have covered all the possibilities. This time we'll work in an atmospheric layer whose lapse rate exceeds one degree C per 100 meters. Say it is 1⅓ degrees per 100 meters. This situation could be found in the lower layers over the desert in the heat of the day. In this case, while our rising air in the balloon is being cooled by expansion by one degree, it has, as before, changed environments. This time its environment at 100 meters above the ground, however, will be 1⅓ degrees colder than the environment it had at the ground. This is ⅓ degree cooler than the balloon's temperature at 100 meters. No need to push this balloon. It now has positive buoyancy forces acting on it. It's going to go up all by itself. (Fig. 4)

We can summarize our findings as follows: Whether or not air is going to resist being pushed up the slope of a mountain depends upon how the air is stratified in the vertical with respect to temperature.

(a) If its temperature lapse rate is less than one degree C per 100 meters it will resist an upward push.

(b) If its lapse rate is greater than one degree C per 100 meters it will favor an upward push.

(c) If its lapse rate is just exactly one degree C per 100 meters it will be neutral, neither resisting nor favoring an upward push.

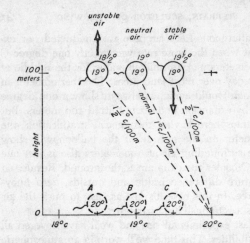

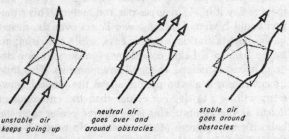

unstable air
keeps going up

neutral air
goes over and
around obstacles

stable air
goes around
obstacles

FIG. 4. *The sketch shows why the stability or instability of air depends upon how the temperature differs from level to level in a layer of air. A, B, and C represent small parcels of air in unstable, neutral, and stable layers respectively. Each is displaced vertically by 100 meters, and each cools 1° C by expansion due to the reduced pressure at the new location. A is positively buoyant here (surrounding air is cooler, denser). B is neutrally buoyant (has same temperature as its new environment). C is negatively buoyant (has an air environment cooler than itself). We see that A is in an unstable layer, one which favors vertical motions within it. C is in a stable layer, one which opposes vertical motions. And B is neutral, developing no buoyancy forces by virtue of vertical displacement.*

To round out our experiment, though, we should ask one more question: what do you suppose would happen if we pushed air down instead of up? Go through the experiment again, only this time start out up at 100 meters above the ground with the temperatures the same inside and outside the balloon. Then move it down 100 meters. Using the same reasoning you will come to the interesting conclusion that case (a) which resisted an upward push also resists a downward push. So no matter which way you push this air, up or down, it tends to return to its original position. We, therefore, call it stable. And case (b) which favored an upward push also favors a downward push. So no matter which way we push on air having this stratification it tends to keep on going in that direction, always getting further from its initial position. So we call it unstable. And case (c) turns out to be neutral to both upward and downward pushes, neither resisting nor aiding.

You can well imagine how differently stable and unstable air behave upon meeting a hill. The stable air in trying to avoid ups and downs gets steered around it; the unstable air leaps joyously over it. You've seen such leaping when you have observed a string of puffy cumulus clouds stretching off downwind of an isolated hill. Just a bunch of atmospheric corks set off on the upwind wide of a hill and carried off by the wind—typical behavior in an unstable atmospheric layer. And you have seen the steering of stable air around obstacles if you have seen the fog flowing in through the Golden Gate or banked up against the coastal mountain ranges like water behind a dam.

Now, it happens that it is more usual for the air to be stably stratified than it is for it to be unstable. You recall that the typical lapse rate is about ⅔ degree C per 100 meters. Since that is less than one degree C per 100 meters it is stable. Consequently, most of the time the air tends more to move around obstacles than over them. Much of the detail that we see in the Los Angeles wind field is the result of the air's twisting and turning to avoid having to go up and over the hills and mountains in the area. Los Angeles, like San Francisco, is notable for having extremely stable air in the lower few thousand feet of the atmosphere, so the effect there is usually quite marked.

Similarly the terrain in your locality imposes its constraints upon the flood of air moving over it. But it is the stability or instability of the flood of air itself that determines the nature of the constraint. It is that which prescribes either back-and-forth motion around obstacles or up-and-down motion over them.

And how are you, an amateur without radiosonde or aircraft, to find out whether air is stable or unstable? In most places the best indicator available is the visibility (how far you can see through the atmosphere). Since stable air discourages vertical motions of air, it inhibits the stirring of dust, smoke, or any other pollutant up into the upper layers of the atmosphere. Thus these restrictors of visibility are confined to a shallow layer of air just above the ground. Unstable air, on the other hand, is quite amenable to vertical mixing motions and quickly distributes atmospheric contaminants, natural and man-made, through great depths of the atmosphere, thus diluting the contaminants to such a low level that they are scarcely detectable. So, as a very rough rule you might say that poor visibilities go with good steering of the air by the terrain, whereas good visibilities go with poor steering but excellent lofting up and down of the air. Have you noticed the beautiful clearness of the air on days when the sky is full of towering cumulus clouds? There are other factors that determine the concentration of pollutants in the air, such as the strength of the wind itself as well as the strength of the pollution sources. The rule is far from infallible. We'll attempt to unravel some of these complexities later on when we discuss smog.

Armed with these simple rules about the stability of the air and the steering by the terrain, you may be able to make some sense out of the winds in your neighborhood. On the other hand, you frequently may find the rules contradicted by your observations. In most localities there is more to the pattern of the local winds than the sculpturing practiced on the general flow by the uneven surface of the earth. There are forces fashioned locally that of themselves can make the air move. We must understand these if we are to get better coincidence between our rules and our observations.

Before going on to a discussion of these local wind generating forces, let me recount for you a few examples of terrain steering that I have observed. They may remind you of better examples that you yourself have experienced. The simplest and most straightforward bending of the wind to suit the will of the mountains that I have seen occurs regularly on an island off the coast of southern California, Santa Catalina. Here a stable layer of air comes in from the Pacific, previously untroubled by any obstacle higher than the cresting waves. Suddenly it encounters a mountainous island, 1000 or 2000 feet high and 20 miles long. But this little mountain range out in the ocean has a low pass in it, an isthmus. The winds whistle through there with speeds maybe double that of the wind over the open ocean. I say "maybe" because I really don't know. There is no wind instrument there. As a matter of fact, I have never stood on the Isthmus and felt the blast of these winds. The only time I was there it was a dead calm, an unusual afternoon, but the evidence of the previous torrents of air was all about me in the form of distorted vegetation. You have probably seen trees and shrubs that grow in an area where strong winds from one particular direction are the rule. All the branches trail off on the downwind side of the trunk. None grows in the upwind direction. The shrubs have the look of having been brushed down onto the ground in the downwind direction. Well, through the Isthmus of Catalina Island the path of the strong winds from one side of the island to the other is marked out with just such deformed vegetation. If one were to choose a home site in the area he might do well to read the message spelled out by these remarkable wind indicators.

The most complicated bending of wind by terrain that I have ever seen occurs in the High Sierra—the crazy buffeting you can get down among the craggy peaks. Here too there are some excellent wind indicators. Perhaps you have looked down on an otherwise placid lake and seen the wind roughened patches of water picking up the glint of the sun. Such patches mirror in scrupulous detail the location of the strong winds over the lake. The High Sierra is generously sprinkled with lakes, little turquoise jewels set deep among the granite peaks. What elaborate fanciful shapes are etched by the wind on these lakes as capricious winds play about the ridges and chasms. The invisible winds up among the peaks glance off the cliffs and down onto the lakes putting telltale scuff marks on their surfaces, rapidly changing areas whose travels over the lake document the changing pattern of the terrain-tortured winds.

Finally, I must tell you about the most spectacular example of stable air channeled through a pass that I have encountered. I know it is not the world's champion. You may have seen better. But it happened in such a beautiful setting that I am compelled to describe it for you. It occurred several years ago in the Andes in western Argentina. We were taking a day's drive up into the mountains in a jeep. First we had to climb a long steep switch-back road up Uspallata Pass. This is a pass that Charles Darwin ascended over 130 years ago, and he described it in his book, *Voyage of the Beagle*. Near the top there was a building which he described as, "the solitary hovel which bears the imposing name of Villa Vicencia." Only in his description of this building does his picture vary from the scene we surveyed here over a century later. Villa Vicencia now is an impressive hotel beside a stream in a narrow valley. The imposing name Villa Vicencia is much celebrated. Water from the stream goes into bottles, and the bottles carry the "imposing name" of that "solitary hovel" to every restaurant in the whole of Argentina.

Shortly after passing Villa Vicencia we reached the summit and began a long descent into a valley also bearing the name Uspallata. It is a little green gem of a valley this time of year (summer) nesting just back of the first ranges. To the east and north the Pre-Cordillera rises to heights in excess of 12,000 feet; to the west stand the loftiest peaks in the western hemisphere, including Aconcagua, the highest of all at 22,834 feet. Weeping willows bordering lush green fields and a gurgling stream full of clear cold water from the snow fields far above furnish this favored place with an aura of Shangri-La. Time-eroded adobe huts and rustic fences of twigs and branches bespeak a remoteness from the modern world. Down this verdant valley on this day moved a late-afternoon breeze, the cool harvest from the now shady west side of the massive mountain bulwark to the west. The green skirts of the willows trailed out at a conspicuous angle in the breeze. The stream leaves the valley through a narrow gorge of its own fashioning, the valley's only exit. Just at this point the road we were traveling crossed a bridge. As we drove up the approach to the bridge the jeep was suddenly accosted by a blast of wind that jolted its four dusty travelers to wide-eyed attention. What a wind! My sons just had to get out and revel in this gale. At this moment their inclination coincided exactly with mine. They first stood on the bridge approach and leaned at an alarming angle into a wind so strong and steady that they could hold the frightening pose for what seemed minutes. Then they went down below to explore the river bank where knee-length grass was completely flattened to the ground by the gale. What excitement! How I wish we had had an anemometer with which to take the measure of this prodigious mountain blast.

I am by no means certain, of course, that this sudden blast wasn't some sort of freak occurrence, repeated only rarely. But I think not. It seems likely that the cold air collected in the deep bowl-shaped Uspallata Valley might be channeled at these speeds through its only, and quite narrow and deep, outlet—the gentle down valley breeze coming to life just as a wide slow river does when it shoots through a narrows. If my presumption is right this gale, sculptured by the valley's narrow exit, really had its beginnings up on the shaded slopes. Many of the local winds that you and I feel have their birth in the local environs. It's time now for us to look into such beginnings.

Chapter 6

WHY THE BREEZES

So far we have been talking mostly about what happens to air already in motion when it encounters terrain obstacles. Now we must consider a different sort of phenomenon, the wind that can develop from scratch in the local area. In other words, we now turn to air put in motion by purely local forces, winds that would develop even though the large-scale (global) flow pattern might prescribe a complete calm for the area.

To start with we must ask the basic question: what is it that pushes the air horizontally? On ancient maps you may have seen, somewhere way out in the ocean, the picture of a very determined looking character with bulging cheeks blowing a great wind through his pursed mouth. Apparently that was the answer the ancients gave to our question. Nowadays we don't need our friend with the big cheeks, although he still appears occasionally as decoration on our maps. We know that it is just air which pushes the air. Or to put it a little more accurately, it is the pressure exerted by air on adjacent air that produces motion.

Back in our discussion of buoyancy (page 28) we singled out the cubic foot of air that had a greater pressure upward on its bottom than it had downward on its top. Now we are concerned with how this same cube can have a greater pressure pushing on, say, its north face than it has pushing on its south face. If that happened to be the case, of course, the cube would begin to move horizontally, from high pressure in the north to lower pressure in the south.

It is sometimes difficult to visualize that the same fundamental laws of motion by which we can predict eclipse of the sun and the precise zigzag of colliding billiard balls also describe the capricious rushing about of the atmosphere. When we get out to push our stalled car, we are convinced readily enough of the logic of the notion that force is equal to mass times acceleration. We can feel the force being applied from compressed palms to straining toes, and we see the impotent vehicle pick up speed as we continue to apply the force. Newton's laws of motion all seem so reasonable, now that he has pointed them out for us. But try to convince a skeptic that the same laws apply to the atmosphere. He has never seen air pushing air, not to mention seeing air accelerate as a result. I can't speak for others, but I think examples of the laws of motion in the atmosphere are hard to see not only because the air is normally so invisible, but also because air does not occur as separate bits and pieces, like billiard balls or Chevrolets. Instead, air is continuous and extremely deformable. But the forces are there, and the motions and accelerations are there. When measured accurately, they are found to obey the same laws.

It may be a little disturbing to you that air exerts pressure in a horizontal direction, particularly since it is the weight of the air above bearing down on our cube of air that produces the pressure in the first place. But it does exert pressure in all directions. Air is not rigid. Nothing squashes quite so easily as air. Step on a tomato, for instance. It will squirt out horizontally in response to the vertical force. If you do it with bare feet (recommended) you may get a dramatic demonstration that the tomato can also push back in the direction exactly opposite to the force you are exerting; a stream of tomato juice will squirt up between your toes. Air behaves the same way. If you are averse to such messy experiments, you might jump into the swimming pool once more and note that the water pushes in on you from all sides, not just down on the top of your head. And you push back in all directions, else you would contract and disappear. So, in response to the weight of air above it our cube feels pressure pushing inward on all its faces, and it responds by pushing back with equal force in all directions, including the horizontal.

Our problem now is to find out how the pressure can be different in two places that are separated horizontally (not vertically). Let's consider the source of the atmospheric pressure, the atmosphere's weight. Doesn't the atmosphere above one place weigh just as much as it does above another? No, not necessarily. The atmosphere may be lighter over one place than over another because it is warmer (less dense) at that place. Weighing less, that particular column produces less pressure at the ground. Aha, so we always have low pressures over the hot deserts and high pressures over the cold Arctic. No! Now we're jumping to an unwarranted conclusion. We can't judge how heavy the atmosphere is in one location just by its temperature at the surface. Can you determine the total weight of a stack of packages by the weight of the bottom package alone? The weight of the atmosphere above a given location depends, of course, on the temperature (density) at all levels. The pressure changes that we measure in moving horizontally from place to place depend upon the varying temperature structure of the atmosphere at all levels, from the top to the bottom. A change at any level can result in a pressure change at the ground.

Consider a column of air that stretches all the way from the ground to the very top of the atmosphere, wherever that may be. If you like, it can be that column which stands above a one square foot area on the ground in front of you. Now fix your attention on the bottom cubic foot of air. Do we really mean to say that if we heat that particular cubic foot of air the total weight of the column will change? Yes, we do. Then if the column is lighter it must have lost some mass. Where did it go? Well, the air in our original cubic foot has expanded and now is distributed over a slightly larger volume. Some of the original air got squeezed out beyond the edges of our cubic foot. The total amount of weight supported by the square foot on the ground in front of you has been reduced by the amount squeezed out. There is actually less air above our square foot. So the pressure at the ground will have been decreased by virtue of the heating at this one level.

Now, I can just hear some troublemaker complaining that the heated cube also expanded in the vertical. What effect does this expansion have? Well, it pushes up on the column above it—puts the squeeze on it, too. And, like our tomato, the column responds to a vertical push by losing some mass horizontally. Again, if you are averse to the tomato comparison, consider what happens to the water above your head when you push off the bottom of the swimming pool. A column of water the size of your head doesn't rise above the pool surface directly over you. Instead, a certain amount of water moves horizontally away from the column above your head as you ascend, just enough to leave the surface undisturbed until you reach it. So, by virtue of heating the lowest layer of a column of air, we force mass horizontally out of the column not only at the level of the heating but at levels of air above it as well. This loss of mass causes pressure at the ground to fall.

But I see our troublemaker is at work again. He wants to know what happens to the mass that got squeezed out of our column. The answer is simple. The mass was squeezed into the surrounding air. Yes, this movement increases the total mass of the neighboring air and pressures rise at the ground in these areas surrounding the heated air. So, as pressures fall over heated areas they rise apace over the surrounding terrain and a horizontal difference in pressure is established between the heated and unheated areas. In response to this horizontal difference in pressures the air moves in toward the heated area. But this heating also produces a vertical force, buoyancy, that at the same time causes the air to rise over the heated area. So the horizontal and vertical forces caused by the heating work together to produce three-dimensional air motions, horizontal breezes that move in toward the heated area linked in perfect harmony with rising air motions above.

You can go through the same line of reasoning for an air column that is cooled at the bottom. The result is just the opposite of the situation we have described—descending motion above the area and horizontal breezes out away from it. So it is by analysis in these terms that we may view the surface of the earth with its many hot and cold spots on the local scale—air at the ground moving from cold to hot, rising above the hot and sinking above the cold. Knowing that the air is continuous (no holes allowed), we can properly infer that somewhere aloft air must move from the areas of rising warm air to those of the sinking cold air to make the picture complete.

Such air circulations induced by heating or cooling are called convective and can be found all over the world and in all shapes and sizes. Even the large scale winds that sweep around the cyclones and anticyclones are but parts of huge, complicated convection cells, the largest of which are practically continental in dimension. At this scale the winds don't move so directly from cold to warm at the surface but tend to spiral out from the one and in toward the other, this due to the earth's rotation. Fortunately for our discussion of breezes that last only a fraction of a day, the effect of the earth's rotation scarcely has time to be felt. It usually is detectable as a tendency for the air to turn to the right a little (to the left in the southern hemisphere) as time progresses. (Fig. 5)

Complicated as they are, these great convective motions, the cyclones and anticyclones, arise from the dif-

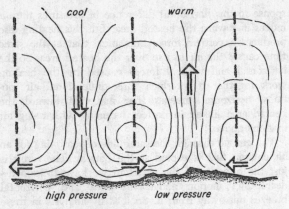

Convective cells

Fig. 5. *Cold or warm spots on the surface of the earth create pressure differences which cause air to converge toward the warm areas, diverge from the cold, as illustrated in this simplified model of convective cells.*

ference in heating between the equatorial and polar regions of the earth, just as surely as Los Angeles' sea breeze is the result of the different heating between the land and the sea near the local coastline.

Many sorts of local temperature contrasts can develop besides those of sea versus land, and each can produce its own breeze. For instance, the slopes of mountains during the day generate an envelope of air over them that is warmer than the air over the valley at the same elevation. Hence we have the valley breeze, from valley to mountain, analogous to the sea breeze, from sea to land. At night, when the situation is just reversed, with excessive heating, we have the mountain breeze in the opposite direction, analogous to the land breeze, from land to sea.

To test these ideas around your own stamping grounds you have but to find places where sizable differences in surface temperature develop. You'll need no thermometer to detect the sort of differences involved. It doesn't require scientists and supersensitive thermometers to discover that the streets, pavements, masonry, stucco, and plaster, plowed fields, bare rocks, and sand get a lot hotter on a sunny day than do green fields, forests, lakes, meadows, and oceans.

If these areas of hot and cold surfaces are scattered about your general environment a chaos of small convective cells will be developed. Their horizontal winds will be too weak to be detected by means at your command. If the hot and cold surfaces are extensive, however, and meet along a well-defined boundary, like the seacoast, you will be able to detect the local breeze that develops. Only the big, well-developed temperature contrasts provide winds of any consequence. The best example, of course, is the seacoast on a sunny day. But even there the effect can be undetectable if a strong wind fashioned by a passing cyclone or anticyclone happens to oppose it. The moral of the story is: don't do hunting for local winds arising from surface temperature contrasts on windy days. These, on the other hand, are good days on which to look about for local winds produced by terrain acting as obstacles. Chances are the local winds in your area are some combination of the two effects. Which effect predominates on any given occasion will depend on the large scale weather: cloudy or clear has an all-important bearing on the development of thermal contrasts at the surface during the day; windy or calm dictates whether there will be a flow for the terrain to twist and turn; stable or unstable decides whether the flow gets deflected around or up and over the terrain. And, of course, to add more complexity to the local winds there are the rising and setting of the sun to alter the pattern of heating and cooling on a daily schedule that sees hot and cold spots changing places from night to day. The ingredients that nature provides for the local winds are seen to be both numerous and variable. Small wonder that the local wind should change not only from season to season and week to week but from day to day and hour to hour.

Let's consider now a few examples of winds that result from differential heating and cooling of the air next to the ground. You have observed such winds many times if you live in hilly terrain. On a clear calm night you have noticed the drift of cool air down off the slopes. These movements are often referred to as drainage winds because they behave like a fluid flowing downhill. They are very common. I have even observed them at sea where, of course, there is no terrain. But on those occasions terrain some distance off was responsible for the formation. The most striking such case happened off the coast of the large island of Hawaii.

We had been at sea for twenty-four days in the University of California's oceanographic research vessel, *Horizon*, most of the time spent within 10 degrees of the equator. We had become accustomed to the hot humid atmosphere of the tropical Pacific. The day before we had seen the fathometer begin a slow, steady rise, from a bottom at 18,000 feet below sea level. The oceanographers on board advised us that we were seeing the submerged flanks of those great twin volcanos, Mauna Loa and Mauna Kea, which together make up the Island of Hawaii. At sunset we were still too far away to see the island although it rises almost 14,000 feet above the sea. But as I rolled out of my cot in the balloon shelter the next morning, there it was in the predawn light. I was surprised at the seemingly low profile of the island. It didn't look half its actual height. But the next surprise came with a chill. For the first time in weeks I was shivering—in midsummer in the tropical Pacific, only 19 degrees from the equator. It was a 3- or 4-knot breeze that chilled me, and it was coming directly from the island, a cool drainage flow from the broad gentle slopes of Mauna Loa. This air probably was only a few degrees colder than the air to which we had become conditioned over the past few weeks. It poured past us on its way out from the island like syrup off a stack of pancakes.

The chilly breeze didn't last long. Before the sun had been up for two hours the flow had reversed completely. By noon a line of cloud had formed halfway up the slopes, now warmed by the sun. The sea breeze had pushed air far enough up the slopes to form clouds (cooling by expansion). The terrain was simple and uncomplicated, as were the winds. The chill of the air unmistakably labeled the land breeze as did the clouds the sea breeze. One couldn't ask for a more elegant demonstration of the influence that night and day exercise on the daily rhythm of local winds.

Some years later I encountered this Hawaii situation turned just inside out. It was in the Tunuyan Valley in western Argentina. Whereas the nocturnal land breeze diverged from the Hawaiian volcano, here the nighttime drainage winds from the surrounding slopes converged on the valley center, where an invisible lake of cold air accumulated. It completely inundated the orchards and vineyards, sometimes to their detriment. But shortly after sunrise the complete reversal occurred as the now-warmed slope air diverged away from the center of the valley. Here the daytime upslope flow formed no cloud, the air being much too dry. This part of Argentina is really a desert—isolated from the Pacific moisture by the formidable Andes (over 20,000 feet). But some of the moisture that the peaks intercept in the form of snow eventually reaches the desert in tumbling torrents after melting. The local farmers divert the rivers for irrigation, and a greenery of vineyards and orchards carpets part of the stark desert landscape. (Fig. 6)

As is true of so many phenomena in nature, it is not easy to find many pure and simple breezes of thermal origin. Superimposed complications tend to distort, exaggerate, and camouflage. The sea breeze where I live is a good example. It gets steered around by the coastal mountains in some places (Malibu) so that it is more nearly parallel to the coastline than perpendicular to it. Inland some twenty miles it diverges where it meets

Mountain wind (night)

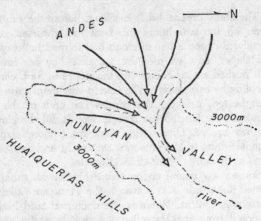

Valley wind (day)

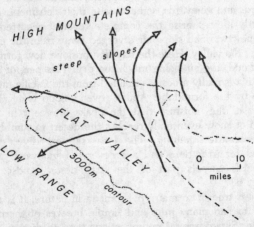

FIG. 6. *An excellent example of the complete reversal of air flow patterns with the change from day to night is found in the Tunuyan Valley, in the foothills of the Andes. Arrows show how the winds sweep down the cooled slopes into the valley at night but rush up the heated valley slopes during the day.*

headlong the San Gabriel Mountains, one branch taking an abrupt left turn of 90 degrees, the other a 45-degree right. Both finally enter the inland deserts through various mountain passes. But somewhere along the line it becomes more of a valley-to-mountain breeze than a sea-to-land breeze. Indeed, from the beginning it is somewhat of a combination of thermal effects, sea versus land, mountain slope versus coastal plain, coastal plain versus high desert—a bewildering confusion of thermal contrasts. And so it must be to some extent with the majority of sea breezes. Certainly San Francisco with its narrow Golden Gate as entry for the sea air and its fingered bay reaching in around coastal hills and mountains boasts an elaborately patterned sea breeze. Its sea breeze blends gradually into an odd collection of up-valley winds. It eventually feeds air into the great central valley of California. Part of this air is deflected southeast along the San Joaquin and after some 200 miles of travel over the vineyards, orchards, and fields is lofted up over the Tehachapi Mountains into the Antelope Valley to join a current of soiled air coming up from the Southwest—air which a few hours earlier was cool and moist with the scent of the sea as it passed my window here in Los Angeles.

Chapter 7

THE UPS AND DOWNS

It's the ups and downs of air flow that fashion most of our weather, whether it be world-wide, local, or microscopic in scale. Without them the fleecy cumulus clouds would be unknown to us. The thunderhead with its attendant electrical displays would be beyond our wildest imagination. No clouds would pile up over tropical islands to guide the Polynesian navigator. No banner cloud atop Mount Fujiyama. Only completely featureless fogs or low overcasts would relieve the monotony of a bright cloudless sky.

But we do have vertical motions in our atmosphere and the endless variety of clouds, sky, and weather that they manufacture. The evidence of ascent and descent is everywhere around us, even in the absence of clouds and cyclones and hurricanes. The scrap of paper lofted in a gusty wind, the gull soaring effortlessly along the cliffs, the up-then-down meander of smoke from the chimney—all these are eloquent, if circumstantial, in their testimony. And there is much vertical motion that goes undetected except by the meteorologists. As a matter of fact, those tremendous sheets of high and middle cloud that sometimes stretch from horizon to horizon are but a part of vast areas of updraft associated with cyclones, so extensive that they can be identified only on weather maps or by weather satellite. In trying to survey them we suffer from a lack of view and perspective, much as the flea on the elephant. It is one of the ironies of modern meteorology that we cannot measure directly the expansive but gentle updrafts of the mature cyclone. They are usually widespread enough to blanket several states at a time. But their vertical velocities are very small, only a matter of a few inches per second in a typical cyclone. However, that's all it takes to flood the streets and rain out ball games.

You and I are more familiar with updrafts on a much smaller scale, that of the cumulus cloud, a column of rising air perhaps a mile or two across and of comparable height. If you have ever afforded yourself the luxury of lying on a grassy hillside beneath a blue sky for half an hour or so to watch a few fresh white cumulus clouds, you have seen these updrafts. They push up those bulging mounds in the top of the cloud. Though appearing to mushroom up with tantalizing slowness, their movements are at speeds of the order of 10 or 20 miles per hour. Unfortunately, many updrafts, almost as vigorous as these, are quite invisible. They are the ones that occur when the air is too dry to form clouds. But the passengers on aircraft flying through them feel their presence. Even though there isn't a cumulus in sight, the experienced air traveler learns to expect bumpy afternoon air on clear warm days.

These cloudless updrafts set off by daytime heating of the ground are called thermals. Perhaps you have seen a hawk, wings motionless, circling up and up until he is but a speck in the sky. His airy spiral traces out with easy precision the dimensions of such a thermal. How the pilots of sailplanes envy his uncanny ability to seek out these completely invisible updrafts. There are even times when parachute jumpers could use his savvy. I know one who once suffered for lack of it. He was a freshly graduated technician from a parachute packing school at an air base in southern California. By the custom of the day, the new graduate was required to jump in a chute he had packed himself. For reasons I have forgotten, the only chute available for him to pack was a large one. And he was a very small fellow. He passed the crucial part of the test nicely; the chute did open when he pulled the rip cord. But the large chute with the light load was at the mercy of thermals. Before he reached the ground, he got caught in one after another. Up and down he went, like a yo-yo on a 3000-foot string. The ground crew in a jeep chased him for miles across the desert before the atmosphere finally let him go. If he had been able to see those thermals, or sense them as the hawk seems to, he could have steered around them.

Actually, you can see some thermals, those whose surface winds are strong enough to pick up dust (if there is dust to pick up). They are called dust devils. They are common in desert areas during the heat of the day—twisting columns drifting across the landscape, kicking up sand, dust, and small debris as they pass. Meteorologists still have much to learn about them. How do they develop the rapid whirling motion? Why are they the size that they are? Why do some turn clockwise, others counterclockwise? Fascinating questions still awaiting final answers. (Fig. 7)

There are some tentative answers about thermals. The source of their updrafts is air that has been heated and become buoyant. The source of their rotation probably is accidental at its inception, a chance turning of air as it moves around a small obstacle or as one side of it is held back by the friction of a clump of trees while the other moves easily across smooth level terrain. In any event, this initial turning, whether clockwise or counterclockwise, is accelerated when the air moves in toward the center of rotation, just as your speed of rotation increases when you are spinning on a piano stool and suddenly draw in your arms. The air is drawn into the center as an indispensable part of the total flow pattern in which heated surface air moves in at the ground to feed the buoyant updraft at the center. The updraft becomes a rapidly twisting narrow column of air.

Have all thermals this twisting motion? Maybe not. Most of them go unseen. Who knows what variety of thermals makes up the bumpy and often dustless air that buffets the light airplane? Precise measurement of their motions is only just beginning. Often these inves-

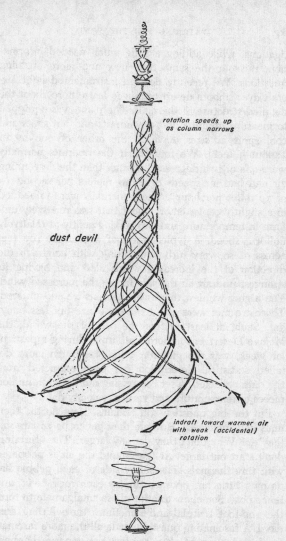

rotation speeds up as column narrows

dust devil

indraft toward warmer air with weak (accidental) rotation

FIG. 7. *The familiar dust devil is a good atmospheric illustration of the principle of the conservation of angular momentum. The closer the rotating air approaches the axis of rotation the faster it spins, just as a person spinning on a piano stool will turn faster if he tucks in his arms and legs.*

tigations, while adding a little much needed information, raise at the same time new and more puzzling questions. We recently flew an instrumented light aircraft over smooth desert terrain to learn more about the detailed structure of thermals. The plane was equipped to measure updrafts and downdrafts and hot spots and cool spots at sizes down to the order of one meter (about 3 feet). We found that the updrafts normally were one or two degrees C warmer than the descending air and had air speeds of a few meters per second (5 or 10 miles per hour). These thermals were imbedded in a slightly cooler environment that was relatively uniform in temperature and was sinking gently at relatively uniform speed. A typical thermal was about 100 feet across or so, very turbulent, tilting with height in the direction of the increased winds aloft and having its strongest updraft on the side facing the increased wind. The higher we flew the fewer thermals we encountered. Those we met were about the same size but less buoyant. Such, at least in this one part of the world, the Mojave Desert in southern California, during a particular week, was the picture. Actually a much more detailed statistical description has been extracted from the data collected, a set comprising more than a million pieces of temperature and vertical velocity data.

But the big question still remains. How do the thermals get organized? How do they get to be as large as they do? Why don't they get any larger? They certainly don't start out large. At the ground the air is peppered with tiny thermals. The sunny side of each pebble has its own little hot updraft as does each rock, twig, and fence post. Somehow or other these amalgamate to form the 100-foot thermal and sometimes the whirling dust devil. A fascinating question made all the more fascinating because we so often see just the opposite happening in nature. A towering column of smoke, say from a smokestack, systematically is dispersed by atmospheric motions; it spreads out, forms wisps that in turn are further shredded by turbulent motions. The organized becomes degraded, disorganized. Of course, to be fair we should admit that this is precisely what happens to our big thermal too, in the end. It eventually is eroded and shredded into oblivion through the wearing action of its atmospheric environment. But the problem of its birth and growth to maturity remains a mystery, an object for further investigation.

It is not always easy to get answers from the atmosphere. Studies of this sort are a good case in point. In order to measure the up-and-down motions of the atmosphere on a scale as small as one meter, we had to measure the vertical motion of the air with respect to the airplane at the same time we were measuring the vertical motion of the plane with respect to the ground. This procedure involved the use of gyroscopes, accelerometers, pressure transducers, a gust probe, and a magnetic tape recorder (14 channels), to mention a few of the basic components. Now complicate these activities further with the temperature measurement problem—that of making a measurement for each meter the plane travels when it is moving at 50 meters per second, about 120 miles per hour. All these add up to fifty temperature readings for each second of flying time. Actually, the temperature measurement was perhaps the easiest problem to solve. Electrical thermometers can be made of very fine platinum wire (0.001 inches in diameter) that respond to temperature changes in as little as 0.01 second. It should not surprise you that one year of work on the instrumentation preceded the one week of actual observations. And were it not for high-speed electronic computers, the analysis of these data would still be going on and would probably continue for another ten years. Instead, it was accomplished within a few months of the experiment.

But there are other vertical currents on the local scale besides the cumulus, the thermal, and the dust devil. These ups and downs that we have been talking about occur normally when the atmosphere is either unstable or only weakly stable. As you will recall from the previous discussion of buoyancy, it is under these conditions that the air moves up and down easily, little or no force being required. But there are some very spectacular up-drafts and downdrafts that can occur when the atmosphere is stable—at times when relatively strong forces have to be exerted to make the air go up and down.

To move the cumulus and thermals in an unstable atmosphere, all that is needed is a little initial push; from then on the vertical motions are self-sustaining. The greater the vertical displacement of a body of air from its initial elevation the greater the buoyancy force in the direction of that displacement. By contrast, a similar initial push in a stable environment results in a buoyancy force that opposes the push. The further the air is displaced the stronger the buoyancy forces oppose further displacement. Even so, stable air often is pushed up thousands of feet. For example, consider the strong current of air sweeping around a vigorous cyclone as it encounters a mountain range. The air, successfully overcoming opposing buoyancy forces all the way, pushes right up to the crest of the mountains. To do so it uses up some of the momentum of the moving current. Going down the other side, however, the buoyancy forces are still acting in the downward direction but now in the direction of the motion, too. The air rushes with accelerated speed back toward its initial elevation. On the way it regains much of the momentum that it lost in going up the mountains.

Associated with the ride up the mountain is a cooling of the air by expansion. Often this cooling is sufficient to cause clouds to form. How many times have you seen clouds obscuring the mountain peaks but the sky perfectly clear everywhere else? Herein lies the explanation of the preference of clouds for the mountains. There is an interesting and important side effect of the cloud formation that aids the air in its flow up the mountain. Had not clouds formed the air would have found it more difficult to attain the crest. The production of heat in the condensing of water vapor in air is involved. Perhaps you are a little more familiar with just the opposite effect, the cooling you experience when water evaporates from your skin (water changing from liquid to gaseous form). When and if this water vapor condenses back into liquid again an equivalent amount of heat is generated and passed on to the environment. When in our mountain example the cloud droplets form, the heat generated is given to the air, which becomes less dense, thus easier to push up the slope. For the same reason, cumulus clouds with the release of this heat of condensation can boom on up to the dimensions of giant thunderstorms, while the dry thermal, deprived of any such extra source of heat and the resulting buoyancy, is limited to much smaller vertical development. Do not underestimate the energy available when water vapor condenses. It drives the most violent storms in the world, the hurricanes and typhoons. It is no accident that these storms are spawned over the tropical oceans just at the time of year when these oceans are warmest. It is then and there that water vapor with its latent heat of condensation is most abundant. Nowhere else on earth is so much of this sort of energy available. Release of this energy in the towering thunderheads and torrential downpours of the hurricane and typhoon generates the awesome winds (in excess of 100 miles per hour at the surface) which in turn drive tortured seas before them to wreak terrible destruction on low lying coastlines. (Fig. 8)

That this latent heat of condensation actually is converted into the sort of warmth you and I can feel is well demonstrated by moist air flowing over a mountain range. If clouds form and rain falls out on the mountain range, the air downwind of the mountain is not only drier than it was upwind but warmer also. It is warmer by an amount representing the heat of condensation of the water lost by the air in precipitation on the mountain slopes. This is why we have the hot deserts inland (downwind) of the mountain ranges along the west coast of the United States, why the chinook sometimes blowing downwind of the Rockies lives up to its Indian name, the "snow-eater." Its heat and lack of moisture can cause vast blankets of snow to evaporate in less than a day.

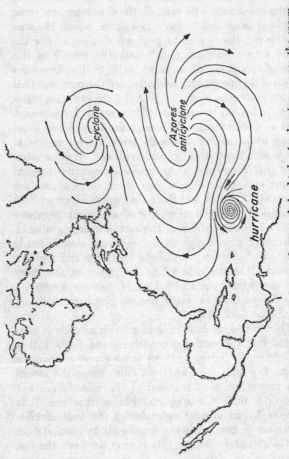

FIG. 8. *The major air movements that might attend the birth of a hurricane over the warm waters of the Caribbean are charted here in simplified form. Release of the latent heat of condensation of water vapor supplies the energy to keep the storm going.*

It is interesting to note that terrain sometimes causes air to be lifted in a much less direct way. For example, very stable air upon encountering a hill resists being pushed up and over; instead, it takes the easy way, splitting into two streams of air that go around either side of the hill. In some cases these streams meet almost head on in the lee of the hill (convergence) and on impact create a very marked updraft. This convergence happens in at least three places along the southern California coast near Los Angeles.

Over the San Fernando Valley opposing sea breezes that have come around opposite ends of the Santa Monica Mountains meet to form a line of updraft. The vertical motions are not so spectacular, but a sharp change in visibility is created between one stream which passes over populated areas and the other which doesn't. Smog is lifted up along this convergence line. Pilots of light aircraft often report updrafts. A much more impressive line of convergence exists in the lee of the Santa Ana Mountains on the opposite side of Los Angeles. Here again a polluted stream of air meets an unpolluted one almost head on. The vertical motions are so strong and well organized that the area has become a favorite spot for soaring in sailplanes. The experienced sailplane pilot can sometimes soar for hours back and forth along this so-called smog front, also referred to as the Elsinore convergence zone. The third such updraft is formed where two unpolluted streams of air directly from the Pacific are brought together. The Palos Verdes Hills, which jut out into the Pacific in the face of the daytime sea breeze, separate the streams. The stable marine air divides upwind of the 1500-feet-high hills, and after a detour of only a few miles around the two separated streams meet again behind the hills. (Fig. 9)

I didn't know about this convergence until one day when making a landing at Torrance Airport, in the lee of the Palos Verdes Hills. I had cut power for the usual glide down to the end of the runway, but as I approached the field I didn't seem to be losing altitude. I

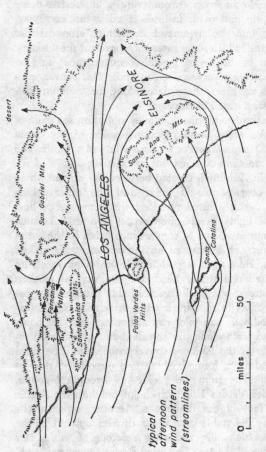

Terrain effect on stable air — Marine air over Los Angeles basin

FIG. 9. Stable marine air flowing inland around both sides of obstacles meets in areas of convergence in the San Fernando Valley, behind the Palos Verdes Hills, and at Elsinore.

checked the throttle. It was closed. The nose of the airplane was pointing down at the proper angle. The air speed was okay. What's wrong here? I was passing the end of the runway and still 800 feet off the ground! That crazy airplane would not go down. Then suddenly, too late to land on this pass, we started descending. I had run into the updraft formed behind the hills. The plane had been sinking through air which itself was rising at about 600 feet per minute. I quizzed the local pilots about this updraft and found it to be a fairly common occurrence. Some time later I learned that in the early days this area had been the site of much sailplaning. Leave it to the sailplane pilots to smell out the good updrafts.

The most powerful updrafts normally do not have such simple sources. They arise from some combination of several of the effects that we have discussed: heating from below, convergence of winds, terrain lifting, the release of latent heat of condensation. Some of these effects, or all, are involved in thunderstorms, where we find some of the strongest updrafts we know about. After all, thunderstorm updrafts are sometimes strong enough to support hailstones the size of a small apple. Have you ever seen what a severe hailstorm can do to a growing crop? I have, only once. I'll never forget the experience. It was in the grape vineyards of western Argentina. The hailstorm was of such severity that the vineyards were reduced to nothing but an expanse of naked white vines. For miles around every last leaf and shred of bark had been polished off. Some of the full-grown poplar trees bordering the roads were snapped off above the ground. Newly eroded gullies ran along the low places, 10 or 15 feet deep and about as wide. Complete destruction. Just a week earlier we had seen these same vineyards resplendent in their full new growth of green leaves. No gullies then, no trees snapped off. What a thunderstorm it must have been. What winds. What rains. And what hail. Most of all, what strong and persistent updrafts to have generated hailstones capable of such destruction!

Chapter 8

WAVES IN THE AIR OCEAN

The most elegant patterns of vertical motion in the atmosphere are those that make the waves in the sky. You see them every time you see a cloud with a corrugated or ribbed structure. Each corrugation or rib is the crest of a wave; the upward displacement of the air has caused enough extra cooling to form cloud where it previously didn't exist or to thicken it where it already had existed. If the air is not very moist no cloud forms at all in the crests of these waves, but the crests are there, though invisible. They come and go unnoticed unless a plane happens to pass through them. The bumps tell the pilot he is in a patch of clear air turbulence. Why does the air become wavy like this in some places some of the time? And what gets the waves started in the up-and-down pattern? Good question.

Let's consider the physics of waves on water and then see if the same physics applies to the atmosphere. As a favor to those of you who do not live near the sea or even a lake, we will take for our laboratory the water in the bathtub. If you favor showers as opposed to tub baths, you will have to exercise your imagination. There are probably few among us who have not mixed a little playful sloshing along with the scrubbing. You no doubt have noticed that it is quite impossible to keep the water level slanted from one end of the tub to the other. By sliding back and forth in the tub it is easy enough, however, to get the water to tilt momentarily.

Indeed, it takes restraint to keep from overdoing it and sending a cresting wave out over the end onto the bathroom floor. It is apparent that the water, once started, likes to go back and forth and up and down. It is equally apparent that it doesn't like to remain tilted with one end higher than the other. The explanation of these preferences follows directly from basic physical concepts we discussed in earlier chapters. (Fig. 10)

When our bathtub wave sloshes back and forth from one end of the tub to the other, water is being transported. At the moment one end of the tub is deep and the other is shallow, the water pressure at the bottom of the tub at the deep end is greater than the pressure at the same level in the shallow end. As in our earlier swimming pool experiments, the greater the mass of water above a point the greater the pressure exerted by the water at that point. In our present tub experiment the result is a horizontal pressure difference between the two ends of the tub, and this difference forces the water to move toward the shallow end. The sloping surface of the water becomes less steep with the departure of water from the deep end and the arrival of more water in the shallow end. In a very short time interval this transport of water will have equalized the depth at both ends. At this precise moment a horizontal pressure difference no longer exists. Is this then the end of our wonderful waves? All tub sloshers know it isn't. The water subsequently builds up to a new crest in what was formerly the shallow end, even though it must move against an opposing pressure force, which its own increasing depth produces. What goes on here?

Well, at the time the water surface became level and the horizontal pressure force vanished, the water was moving rapidly from one end to the other. The water had a lot of momentum, just as a car has when it is coasting at 50 miles per hour along a level road. Turning off the engine doesn't bring the car to a sudden stop. So it is with the water. It uses up its momentum piling up at the end of the tub as your car might come to a

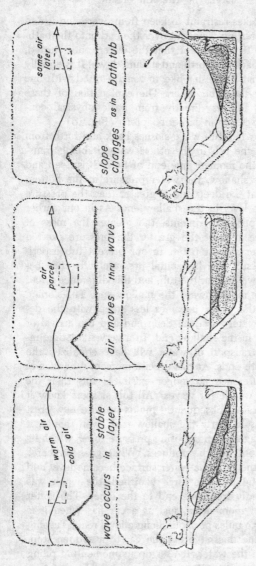

FIG. 10. Your bathtub is an admirable laboratory for studying the behavior of fog waves, or atmospheric waves in general. Movements of the water as you slosh back and forth resemble the movements of air parcels under buoyancy and horizontal pressure difference forces. Here the analogy is between the bathtub wave and the air wave in a stable layer to the lee of a hill.

The mountain wave

halt by rolling up a steep incline. When the water comes to a stop, one end high the other low, the process is immediately reversed because of the now reversed pressure force acting on the water. Again, we may use the analogy of your car, which has just rolled to a stop on the steep incline. If you have no brakes it will immediately start rolling backward down the hill.

So, the sloshing back and forth and up and down perpetuates itself and if left alone dies down only because of the friction of water against tub and the friction of water against water. A little back and forth encouragement from the tub's occupant is quite enough to make up for the frictional losses, and just a little bit too much by an overenthusiastic novice quickly sends water over the dam and onto a soggy bathroom mat.

Perhaps water sloshing back and forth in a tub will not remind you of anything you've ever seen in the sky. I would have to agree with your skepticism if I had not seen time-lapse photographs of fog surging up the sides of mountains and falling back only to come rushing back again and again, just like the water in our tub. But it takes the special magic of speed-up photography to make the process real. Telescoping time by taking pictures at a rate of one per 6 seconds and projecting them at 16 per second speeds up the action by 6 times 16 or 96 times. Motions of the features of the top of the fog that are imperceptible to the eye look for all the world when sped up 96 times like waves on the open sea. Just as we have microscopes to make visible things that are too small for us to see, we also have the time-lapse motion pictures to make visible motions that are too slow for us to see.

It is a fascinating and often illuminating experience to see things in a different time scale. I've sometimes wondered how our movements must appear to the ants. Are our motions as slow and ponderous to them as their motions are quick and jerky to us? Is the one second time interval between the fall of my right foot and my left as I step over an army of ants crossing the hot sidewalk more like an hour to the ants? Is that split-second hesitation shared by two ants as they touch antennae really a leisurely conversation to them? I, at least, am persuaded that their sense of the passage of time is not what it seems to me, any more than that seemingly almost static gray blanket of fog in the valley below is static at all when seen in the telescoped time scale of the time-lapse camera.

It is a happy circumstance that the time-lapse camera need not be a complicated, expensive piece of equipment purely for scientific research. Very ordinary 8-mm motion picture cameras can be modified to take pictures at the rate of one frame every few seconds. If you have a movie camera that can "single frame" (be operated like a still camera) you merely rig up a device to trip the shutter at the rate you want. With time and patience you can trip the shutter yourself every 5 seconds, or at whatever interval you choose. Just remember, it takes a long time, over an hour and a half of button-pushing at 6-second intervals, to produce one minute of time-lapse movies.

Our house happens to be situated in an ideal place for taking time-lapse movies of fog (but I haven't taken any). The fog below the house sometimes looks very much like the water sloshing back and forth in the bathtub. We look out over a narrow canyon in the Santa Monica Mountains. The canyon is much like a bathtub except that one end is open. Sometimes through the open end a blanket of fog from the Pacific pours into the canyon. Huge swells, 100 feet high or higher, move silently, and ever so slowly, up the canyon, then back down. Sometimes a big soft white swell rises up high enough to inundate us. Suddenly the rest of the world disappears for 5 gray minutes. Then as suddenly it reappears as the wave of fog recedes down the steep slope, much as waves on the beach do after they have made their run up the sandy shore. But what is making these waves? I don't know. It's another interesting puzzle for the meteorologist.

You may have noticed an odd thing about waves. They can have quite improbable beginnings. Contemplate, for instance, the origin of those perfectly circular ripples expanding toward the shores of an otherwise placid pond. That such perfection should so quickly result from the rude splash of a pebble probably doesn't astound you—but it should. Think about it for a minute. Has the splash of the pebble the beautiful symmetry of the waves it generates? Usually not, particularly if it is the typical small piece of rock with all sorts of points and angles and has entered the water at some low angle. Do round rocks make smooth waves and square rocks make angular waves? A silly question! From the shape of the ripple that reaches the distant shore one cannot divine the shape of the pebble. Apparently the pebble's splash is a trigger mechanism only. What happens after the first second or so depends on other things.

The spacing of the waves resulting from such a disturbance and the speed with which they move through the water depend on gravity and the difference in density between the water below and the air above and the depth of the water. The nature of the initiating splash is not important. It matters not whether it be a fish breaking the surface in pursuit of a flying insect or the fisherman's lure hitting the water; either way, the waves come out in perfect circles. What does matter are the characteristics of the fluids (water and air) along whose interface the waves move. Consequently, it is not easy to say just what it is that starts the big waves in the fog in front of our house. Any of a host of disturbances will do. Maybe the very first heating of the hills above the fog and the attendant upslope currents are responsible somehow. Or perhaps the palisades at the coast, like a rock in a stream, give the fog a vertical push to start things off. I don't know the specific answer. But it seems clear that plenty of provocation for wave development is available at the bottom of the atmosphere. The rich and varied terrain of this planet coupled with the restless winds must provide an overabundance of triggers.

We do not see more waves partly because air is invisible much of the time. Furthermore, waves occur only in very stable stratifications. To remind you, this means that waves form only when opposing buoyancy forces accompany the vertical displacement of the fluid. The interface between water and air is a very stable interface. Push up a little water and it becomes negatively buoyant, being much denser than the surrounding air. It tries to return immediately to its former position. So, if you would like to look for waves in the atmosphere, find a place where warm (light) air is positioned directly above cool (heavy) air. The interface between these two is a very stable place where waves can form, in many ways not unlike the ones you see on water. The top of our fog is such a place. The air above is much warmer than the foggy air. Apart from size, the main difference between the fog waves and the bathtub waves is in their speeds. The truth of this was best demonstrated by the necessity for time-lapse photography to reveal the waves in the fog. In other words, we had to speed up our fog waves artificially by about 100 times in order to give them the same apparent motion as water waves. The cause of this slowness is the relative smallness of the restoring (buoyancy) forces at the fog interface; the forces there are about 100 times smaller than the comparable forces at the air-water interface. This disparity is due, of course, to the much smaller differences in density in the fog case. A mass of foggy air shoved up the side of the canyon, like water pushed up the end of the bathtub, is subject to a restoring force, but it's such a weak one in comparison to the water case, the motions are sluggish and almost imperceptible except by time-lapse photography.

Now you should complain. We've ascribed our waves to two sorts of forces: vertical (buoyancy) forces and horizontal (pressure difference) forces. First one, then the other. Well, which is it? It is both, of course. They go hand in hand. And they both derive from the same force, gravity. It is easy to understand then why these waves are known among scientists as gravity waves. But there are lots of waves in the atmosphere that aren't simple gravity waves. Complications arise from the existence of other effects, such as the drag of air on other air moving in a different direction or at a different speed. You have seen the sort of waves that develops when you stir paint in a can, little burbles back and forth that follow in the wake of the paddle. It is particularly noticeable when you are mixing two different colors of paint together. There are occasions when strong jets of air move through slower moving air. The jet stream is a good example, often referred to as a "river of air" in the upper atmosphere (usually 30,-000 or 40,000 feet). That waves sometimes accompany the jet stream is evidenced by the beautiful wave-patterned clouds often seen in the vicinity.

But we haven't mentioned yet the most spectacular waves that occur in the size range that we might call local. They are the mountain waves and, when visible, take the form of lenticular clouds. Each cloud traces out the crest of a wave, the place where rising motions have led to the formation of cloud droplets. These graceful lens-shaped clouds stand motionless down-wind of large mountain ranges, much like the waves you see standing behind a rock in a rapidly moving stream. Even when viewed through the time-telescoping eye of the time-lapse camera the clouds appear stationary. Yet the air is flowing over the mountains at speeds often ranging from 50 to 100 miles per hour. It seems incredible that these clouds can stand still in such circumstances. The air must blow right through them. And that's just what it does. It is this feature of lenticular clouds that requires them to be the result of wave motion in the atmosphere. Perhaps you haven't thought of it before, but this is how waves on the ocean behave. The waves are not tied to the water.

Gulls resting on the surface and seaweed floating in the water bob up and down with each passing wave. The waves approach, pass, and recede in endless procession, leaving the water with its inhabitants far behind. And the cloud that we see in the crest of the mountain wave does not carry its "inhabitants" along with it either. The air turns cloudy upon entering the wave (cooling by ascent) and turns clear upon leaving (heating by descent).

If we change our frame of reference a little, the resemblance between ocean waves and mountain waves will come into focus. Let's free ourselves from the water, get up on a surfboard and ride the ocean waves. Now the water goes rushing by. Look over your shoulder and see the crest of the wave, your constant companion. Now to you the wave is stationary but the water moves. Isn't it interesting how different our fluid environment can seem depending on whether we are at rest with respect to it or are moving past it? The swimmer treading water bobs up and down like a yo-yo while the surfer sweeps along a horizontal path, although both are reacting to the same wave. Remove yourself now to the mountain environment. You stand high on the ridge facing into a strong wind. You look over your shoulder, downwind, and see behind you the graceful sweep of the lenticular cloud, the visible crest of the mountain wave. It is not receding. It's as much a fixed piece of your environment as the granite upon which you stand. Release a balloon (inflated so that it just barely floats) from our mountain top. It (like the seaweed) rises and falls with the waves as it moves off downstream. The sailplane pilot, on the other hand, streaks (like the surfer) along a path parallel to the leading edge of the wave cloud, angling into the strong current of air that sweeps past him up into the cloud behind. (Fig. 11)

The updrafts at the leading edges of lenticular clouds can be quite strong, as much as several thousand feet per minute, corresponding to 20 or 30 miles per hour

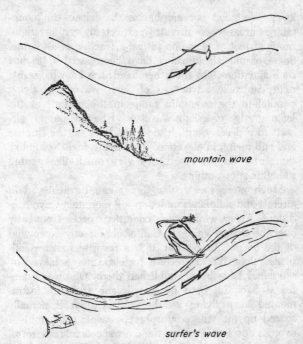

mountain wave

surfer's wave

FIG. 11. *The surfer's view (a relativistic one) of the wave he rides in to shore is the same as the sailplane pilot's view of the air wave he rides downwind of a mountain range. Looking down, both "see" water (air) rushing by, but the wave remains stationary.*

vertically. The downdrafts at the trailing edges can be just as strong. Because of their speeds, they are of more than purely academic interest. The unwary or uninformed pilot flying beneath or through such wave clouds at typical aircraft speeds may subject his craft to severe vertical accelerations when he suddenly enters and leaves the updrafts and downdrafts. Furthermore, he can quite unexpectedly find himself losing elevation at rates as high as half a mile per minute, even though the attitude of the plane remains perfectly straight and level. We need not emphasize the hazard in mountainous areas when aircraft unexpectedly can lose thousands of feet of elevation in just a fraction of a minute. Some of our air disasters have been ascribed to just such situations. On the other hand, the knowledgeable pilot can take advantage of such waves. By flying parallel to the mountain range in the updraft at the leading edge of a long wave cloud he can put his aircraft in a descending attitude, cut back on the throttle and still maintain elevation, thus saving fuel. Not unlike the surfer on his board. It's very much like getting something for nothing.

Much more spectacular things can be achieved in aircraft and sailplanes under strong mountain wave conditions. Every winter such conditions occur frequently over the Owens Valley in California, directly downwind of the Sierra. As a result, it is a favorite spot for sailplane pilots. World's records for elevations achieved by sailplanes have been established there. One was established back in 1950 by a sailplane specially instrumented as a flying weather observatory. It actually soared up into the stratosphere, reaching a height of over 44,000 feet. Perhaps the most spectacular performance was in an old surplus World War II fighter plane, a P-38. You may remember it as the Lockheed Lightning, the one with the twin-boom fuselage. On this day the plane's pilot, who was an experienced sailplane pilot as well, found a region of such strong and persistent updraft that he was able to cut both engines, feather both props, and soar on the wave for half an hour. A high-performance aircraft such as this under normal, no updraft, conditions soars like a rock—striking testimony to the strength of the Sierra wave on this particular day.

We should not leave the discussion of lee waves over mountains without puzzling just a little about why these waves form. Research, such as that done on the Sierra wave in the early 1950s using instrumented gliders and radar and optical tracking of their paths through the waves, has told us much. They are complicated waves, but a good bit of their behavior is that of the gravity waves, of which we spoke earlier. For example, they occur only at very stable layers in our atmosphere, similar to that at the top of the fog, where warm air lies directly above cold. In this situation any vertical push upward, such as a mountain range might provide for a strong current moving perpendicular to it, results in strong opposing (restoring) buoyancy forces. So, in response to the upward push of the mountain range the air first rises then descends. But, due to its downward momentum, it does not stop when it returns to the initial level. It undershoots, much as the water in the bathtub did after the wave receded. And in moving below its initial level it now develops a restoring force that soon stops the descent and starts a new ascent. So a yo-yo motion develops just as it did on the top of the fog and for the seaweed floating in the ocean swells. Opposing this periodic motion is the friction of air on air. As the air moves downwind, this resistance gradually destroys the wave.

Admittedly this is a great oversimplification of the physics of the mountain wave. Many details of the observed flow in these mountain waves are very perplexing, and some sophisticated theories have been developed to explain some of the puzzles. The work continues to bring observation and theory into even closer agreement. New observations and measurements are added to our store of information every once in a while, sometimes quite by accident.

An accidental discovery happened to us a few years ago. While on a shakedown flight to test some new instrumentation for measuring updrafts and downdrafts, we sighted three beautiful wave clouds about 500 feet above the ocean, curving around a headland near Santa Maria, California. Delighted at the prospect of trying out our new equipment on some good ups and downs, we flew the plane through the waves. It was like a ride on a roller coaster. The clouds were the crests of waves sure enough and the clear spaces between them the corresponding troughs.

When we got home and reduced our data we found that the vertical velocities oscillated between 8 miles per hour up and 8 miles per hour down. The waves occurred at an interface between two layers differing in temperature by 23 degrees Fahrenheit (top one warmer, of course). And, as with the mountain waves, the air flow was at right angles to the wave clouds. The clouds remained fixed with respect to the headland, a promontory about 1500 feet high called Point Sal. Even the distance between wave crests, a little less than one mile, agreed with the computed theoretical wavelength of a gravity wave on an interface separating two layers of air at the temperatures measured and moving past an obstacle at 15 miles per hour, the observed wind speed. In every respect except one these three evenly spaced waves followed the familiar pattern. They stood *upwind* of the obstacle, not downwind! But perplexities such as this are the fuel that keeps the fires of progress going. As you read this book, answers have already been suggested to explain why these waves should appear in the air before the air has encountered the obstacle that presumably is to initiate them.

Now we are done talking about why the local atmosphere moves as it does, gets ruffled up as it does. Stability versus instability, heating versus cooling, rough terrain versus smooth terrain—all are mixed together to produce the observed behavior of atmosphere. Will we be able to look at the final product, the local weather, and guess which strings are being pulled behind the scenes?

Chapter 9

THE WEATHER SPECTRUM

The time has come to turn our new eyes upon the
meteorological scene, eyes that now see sun-drenched
hillsides as the manufacturers of upslope breezes and
quiet valleys as river beds for chilly predawn air. These
eyes can still appreciate the soaring of the hawk but
they picture too the towering column of rising air on
which he rides. In their new way of looking upon the
world there is a little more order, a little less chaos, in
the seemingly random distribution of the clouds, wind,
rain, and snow that together make up the local weather.

As an exercise in this kind of "seeing," you are in-
vited to look with me at my home town's weather. It's
probably quite different from yours, but it obeys the
same physical laws. So, with this apology for discussing
my home town instead of yours, let's proceed to ponder
Los Angeles' many meteorological disguises, its all too
usual veil of smog versus the clean fresh-scrubbed look
it wears after the rare winter storm, its fog and stratus
versus its furnace-like Santa Ana wind condition, its
wildfires versus its frosts and freezes—in a word, its
spectrum of local weather.

Every town has its own weather spectrum. Yours is
no exception. In reality there is more than one spectrum. The one we have just mentioned is a time spectrum. That is, it consists of all the different kinds of
weather that parade by if one sits long enough and
lets time pass. One year's weather watching will fairly

well complete your local weather time spectrum, but not altogether. There are some extreme rainstorms, hot spells, cold snaps, and wind storms, the record breakers, that show up only infrequently. So actually your time spectrum is never complete. This is one of the most interesting aspects of meteorology. Time always brings with it new surprises.

The other sort of spectrum that our local weather has is a space spectrum. To observe it we must get up out of our chair and move around in the local environment and notice the changes in the local weather from place to place. There are the hot spots, the cold spots, sometimes dry spots and wet spots, not to mention the clear and cloudy or calm and windy spots. It is the combination of the time and space spectra that comprises the total picture of the local weather. It's a richly patterned picture in four dimensions: three in space and one in time. To fill it in completely you have to move around the local area on many different occasions, under all sorts of weather conditions.

If you live in the Midwest, the time spectrum will be wide and spectacular. In the passing of just one year a remarkable variety of contrasting weather situations will appear. Everything from blizzards to sultry summer heat waves. On the other hand, the space spectrum in the Midwest may be narrow, particularly if you live in the incredibly flat, uniform expanses where the only obstruction to the wind is an occasional tree or building. In southern California the opposite is true. The time spectrum is fairly narrow. The contrasts from day to day and season to season are small by comparison with those of the Midwest. But the space spectrum is wide. The great variety of terrain features and surface conditions provide surprisingly large contrasts in both the horizontal and the vertical.

As a beginning for our examination of Los Angeles' local weather, let's first outline in general terms its weather spectrum—its extent in time and space. As for time, it is not neatly divided into four seasons as the weather is in so many parts of the world. No matter what the season in Los Angeles, chances are three or four to one that the air has come from the mid-latitude North Pacific, and it arrives at the beaches with about the same temperature as the water. From the coldest to the warmest season the water temperature off southern California varies only about 15 degrees F (about 8 degrees C). Small wonder the time spectrum is so narrow. The other 20 or 25 percent of the time the air comes from places capable of greater temperature extremes. Maybe half a dozen times a year the hot dry Santa Ana winds blow in from the high dry deserts to the Northeast. Several times in the summer air from the far-off Gulf of Mexico and the Caribbean arrives over southern California, aloft if not at the ground. Then Los Angeles sees a pale imitation of the hot sultry thunderstorm weather of the Midwest, pale because of the rigors suffered by the air on its long tough journey over the dry mountainous Southwest. Maybe once a year deep moist tropical air comes in from the Equatorial Pacific without suffering the rigors of overland travel. In one such case, in September 1939, southern California even experienced a hurricane.

The coldest weather comes by one of two different routes, one over land and the other over sea. Sometimes in winter the winds from the Northwest are so strong and extensive that frigid air from the Arctic makes a very direct, quick trip across the Gulf of Alaska and down the West Coast, arriving before the ocean has removed arctic chill entirely. The resulting weather is cold, windy, and smogless. But the coldest air that ever comes to southern California (like the warmest) comes from inland. It makes the long difficult trip all the way from the Canadian Arctic—crossing the prairies, the Rockies, the Great Basin, and California's inland mountain ranges. It's such a difficult trip that it isn't achieved every winter, maybe only one in three or four. It happens only when an exceptionally deep layer of cold air invades the Midwest, deep enough to spill over the high continental divide like water over a dam. Then southern California gets subfreezing temperatures and strong winds at the same time, a formidable threat to local agriculture. That, in brief, is the time spectrum—temperate oceanic weather all year long except for very occasional minority reports from the continent and the tropics.

But what elaborate transformations the local terrain impresses on this gaunt time spectrum. The same air which feels and smells of the ocean at the coast becomes in one short day the dry searing air of the Mojave Desert, some 50 to 100 miles inland. And what dramatic contrasts occur in the vertical! A short trip of two or three miles from the beach at Malibu to the top of the Santa Monica Mountains, 2500 feet up, effects a comparable change in temperature and humidity—oceanic air at the bottom, desert-like air at the top. Consequently, the kind of weather that any Los Angeles neighborhood has depends very much on just how far inland it is and what its elevation may be.

Perhaps a good general indication of the kind of climate a particular place has can be inferred from what the youngsters do out-of-doors. They, more than their elders, are out in direct contact with the elements and as such their activities are more shaped by them. The part of the Los Angeles area in which I spent my childhood is about thirty miles inland from the coast, at the foot of the San Gabriel Mountains. Summers there were hot and dry. A summer vacation was a sunny expanse of time to be filled, according to our whims, by hikes in the mountains, backyard projects, and vacant lot adventures. Because of the hot semi-arid climate we possessed a prodigious appetite for getting wet, and sought out every possible place where we could even partially submerge ourselves. To satisfy this passion took a bit of doing thirty miles from the beach in essentially riverless and lakeless southern California. Of course, there was the municipal plunge, but a swim there cost money. Maybe once a week parental permission (and money) would allow the great treat. The rest of the time we were on our own.

Locally there were two sources of water adequate to our needs, if you discount the always available garden hose and washtub. One was the water impounded behind the flood control dams up the steep narrow canyons of the San Gabriels. The other was the muddy effluent from the rock crusher plants down in the Sawpit Wash. These plants used water to wash the dirt from the crushed rock and sand, and it accumulated in the deep pits where the rock and sand had been dug up. Here we had a cool, if muddy, lake in the middle of the hottest and driest of all our landscapes, a boulder-strewn, lifeless (except for snakes and lizards) wasteland. The trouble was that parents considered it dangerous and filthy. Even we admitted it was dirty, but only under duress. You couldn't see your feet through the brown water even if you were standing in it only ankle deep. As a consequence, we were more in need of a bath after a swim than before, regardless of our previous condition.

On the other hand, the water behind the big concrete dams in the canyons was clear and pure. I expect its use for recreational purposes was frowned upon, but in those days there were no fences and everything was friendly and informal between us and the canyon guard, a most kindly civil servant (father of a schoolmate). We built rafts, fished for perch, and splashed around generally behind Sawpit Dam. But we never got enough because it was a hot two-mile hike uphill into the canyon where the dam was. Again, we were more in need of a cool dunking when we got home, than when we had left.

It is curious that this appetite for emersion recurred in the "wet" season, winter. This was the time of year when the dams did the job for which they were intended, impounding water from the extensive watersheds of the San Gabriel Mountains during storms. Canyons without dams loosed raging muddy torrents upon the broad valley after heavy rains, a flood that often undermined houses. But the canyons below the dams usually carried only harmless streams in the wintertime. This was water impounded in a day or two of heavy rain and released gradually over many weeks to soak down into the sand and gravel of the valley floor, later to be pumped up for domestic use. In the long dry sunny spells between the few winter storms we would sometimes seek out the pools in these little streams for off-season splashing. The water was much too shallow to do any swimming, and it was so cold that I can only marvel now at our compulsion to get wet.

Those of you who live with free-flowing rivers and natural lakes and ponds the year round probably cannot appreciate such desperate appetites. I sometimes wonder now, thirty years later, if a similar appetite doesn't account for the recent proliferation of backyard swimming pools. A few decades ago one of the distinguishing features of a wealthy Los Angeles neighborhood as seen from the air was the cluster of turquoise blue swimming pools. Now no such easy index to the affluent society exists. The bright blue spots have spread to neighborhoods of quite modest means. The distribution now is related less to financial solvency than to climate. Affluent Bel-Air, on the cool seaward slopes of the Santa Monica Mountains, former champion, now runs well behind many more modest but hotter areas, such as the San Fernando Valley. The fact that most people with pools don't use them for almost eight months of the year, the colder months, only persuades me that our desert-like climate afflicts us with a touch of irrationality.

I don't know how old I was when I realized that all southern California was not like our neighborhood—hot and dry in the summertime. But I do remember vividly the day that the realization was thrust upon me. It was in hot summer, and we had traveled to a home only a few miles from the beach to visit friends. We arrived at noon, but it was so cool I couldn't believe it.

The world around me was beginning to lose its simplicity. Now, having lived in a variety of locations, inland, at the beach, and several places in between, I accept fully what a remarkable space spectrum the southern California area has. Over the years my shoes have served well as climatic indicators. Old work shoes left unused in the closet for a month or two come into their own peculiar equilibrium with the atmosphere. Inland it was that hard, dry, curled-up condition that makes a rocking chair out of your foot. At the beach it was the opposite, soft, pliable, and green with mildew. In the one location the summer temperature could get up over 100 under a hot sun; in the other it could stay in the low 70s under a gray fog. Fortunately for Los Angeles, there is sufficient compromise between these two extremes to suit the special requirements of all sorts of people and shoes.

Chapter 10

LIFE AND DEATH OF
THE MARINE LAYER

The large-scale weather systems furnish the raw materials from which the local weather is fashioned. Actually it is a large anticyclone that is responsible for most
of Los Angeles' local weather. This system stands off
the coast of California, a couple of miles deep and
2000 miles or so in diameter. Some visualize it as a
huge mountain of air that somehow or other stands
guard over the southwest coast, fending off the swirling
cyclones that sweep across the Pacific on the stormy
westerlies. But really it's not that at all—not a big pile
of air, stubbornly immobile. It exists only in the way
that the waves on the ocean exist, as flow patterns
through which the fluid moves.

If you could fix your eyes on a particular volume of
a fluid in a wave pattern and at one instant call that
particular volume the wave crest, the next moment or
two in time would make you out to be a liar, for the
same volume of fluid would be occupying the trough
position. So it is with the anticyclone. The air enters it,
spirals through and leaves it. In reality the anticyclone
is not weighed out in grams and tons; rather, it is
traced out in the paths that the transient air takes as
it sweeps across the eastern half of the North Pacific
Ocean. The important fact for us is that the air is trans-
formed, given certain properties, while taking the big
tour off our West Coast. (Fig. 12)

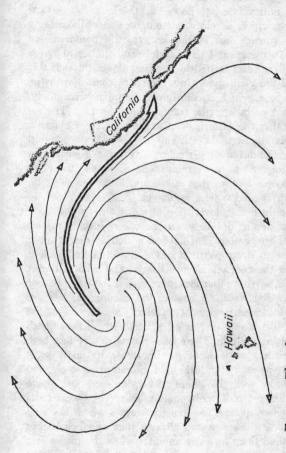

FIG. 12. The almost stationary anticyclone centered northeast of Hawaii influences the weather along the California coast by pouring in a steady supply of cool, moist air.

I like to think of the northeastern sector of this anti-cyclone as a big hot-air factory. For all but the air at the very bottom the paths taken by the air in this part of the anticyclone are downhill. Think of the vertical motions within a pile of dough on a breadboard. As dough spreads out at the bottom, the dough above sinks. In the great Pacific anticyclone the air above is compressed and heated as it passes down through this part of the giant gyre. Only the air in contact with the sea surface, which is constrained to move horizontally, does not partake of the compressional heating. The result is that the eastern Pacific Ocean off the California coast is almost a desert. The air above it is hot and dry except for a very shallow layer at the surface, a layer referred to as the marine layer. This is the layer that people live in, that sailors and fishermen work in, that surfers and swimmers play in.

So only a thin layer of cool moist air, maybe 1000 feet in depth, lies between the ocean surface in this part of the eastern Pacific and a slab of desert air a mile or so deep. What a desert it would be, were it not for the cool sea surface below. And what a desert it is for anything that flies more than a thousand feet or so above the sea. Of course, the commercial jets are air-conditioned, and most travelers are unaware of the desert-like nature of this air through which they climb to cruising altitude. There is no cactus, no dry lake bed, no visible clue whatsoever. But those fortunate souls who fly about in the little light aircraft at 2000 or 3000 feet know well that there is a vast desert just above that shallow, cool, moist marine layer. They wear coats and jackets against the cool sea breezes when they step into their planes at the airports near the beach, but they shed them in a few minutes when the planes rise out of their usual environment into the hot dry desert air above. Temperatures frequently change from the low seventies to near 100 F in a mere few hundred feet of ascent. The transition from marine layer to hot dry layer where this marked increase in temperature occurs is the site of southern California's famous (or infamous) temperature inversion.

You might think it strange that anything except the lowest few feet of the air out in the hot-air factory should be affected by the cool wet ocean surface. Why should the marine layer get to be as deep as 1000 feet? One answer is that the air gets tumbled and turned as it passes over the seas and swells of the open Pacific. When air rides up the crest of a wave it splashes into the drier, warmer air above and, mixing, quickly shares its new-found moisture. At the same time it is replaced at the surface by a wisp of the upper dry warm air which descends to take a swipe at the ocean, maybe tearing a little spray from the top of a peaking wave. This vagrant wisp also acquires a load of moisture and at the same time loses some of its heat. It then gets tossed back into the air to bestow its new coolness and moisture on the air some distance above the surface. Because the marine layer progressively moves toward warmer water during its journey (except for the stretch along the northern California coastline) convective mixing is added to this mechanical stirring. And so the marine layer is built up in the continued turbulent splashing, stirring and mixing that go on for a thousand miles or so over the North Pacific. In an atmosphere of less stability, for example the air over the Caribbean, this mixing can extend up into the atmosphere for several miles. But over this part of the eastern Pacific that upward stirring is inhibited by the warm layer aloft. The moist, cool qualities of the sea surface are confined to only the lowest 1000 feet or so.

So it is that a flood of chilled moist air is delivered to southern California. It tumbles in across the coastline, bringing with it the feel and smell of the sea. Though it may be midsummer with the sun glaring down out of a cloudless sky from a position near the zenith, it is cool in the marine layer along the California coast. Were it not for the benevolence of this thin cool stratum the western deserts would extend to the very beaches. San Francisco would have no fog, Los Angeles no smog, and both far fewer tourists.

But the moderating influence of the marine layer on the climate is confined fairly close to the coastline. Born of the sea, this shallow cool moist layer rapidly withers as it passes over the hostile continent. As soon as it crosses the beaches on the daytime sea breeze it begins to pick up heat from the hot sand. Thermals develop and distribute this heat throughout its depth. The heating continues as the moving air encounters the endless obstacle course of hot pavement, hot masonry, hot fields, hot roofs that the sprawling city and its suburbs put down before it. Where urban sprawl has not yet invaded the terrain, the marine air encounters equally hot granite boulders, sandy loam, sagebrush, yucca, and hillside chaparral. Some days when the marine layer is unusually deep, 2000 or 3000 feet thick, it easily survives the trip across Los Angeles' coastal plain to the foothills of the San Gabriels, 30 or 40 miles inland. The layer being deeper, the available heat is distributed over a greater mass of marine air with the result that the temperature increase is less than it would be for shallower layers. It arrives at the foothills somewhat warmer than it started but still cooler than the air above it. However, the typical marine layer is much shallower, 1000 to 1500 feet thick, so gets much hotter, and just barely survives the rigors of the trip from the coast. It arrives a warm dry ghost of its former self. So the foothill communities boast of a warm dry climate while the beach communities brag about their cool ocean breezes and an immunity from the summer heat.

Even the deep marine layer does not survive the trip over or around the taller mountain ranges to the inland deserts. There the enhanced vertical stirring of the atmosphere (as it encounters rougher terrain) along with the continued heating from below raises the temperature of the marine air to that of the hot dry air above. The boiling, bubbling action of the daytime thermals, formerly confined to the marine layer, now finds it easy to penetrate far up into the deep upper warm layer. Moisture accumulated during thousands of miles of travel over the North Pacific in a shallow surface layer suddenly is lofted in buoyant plumes that penetrate to heights of 10,000 or 15,000 feet and mix thoroughly into the new warm dry environment. So vast is this new environment, five or ten times the marine layer by volume, that the addition of the marine layer's moisture has only a small effect on the resultant humidity. It's almost as if the marine layer were swallowed up without a trace. Now there is but one layer where before there were two. Shallow, cool, and moist have blended with deep, hot, and dry to yield the clear parched atmosphere that courses over the arid wastes of southern California's inland deserts.

Most of Los Angeles' millions, it is true, live inside this marine layer whose character changes in a fairly regular fashion with distance inland. But a few live above it, those who inhabit the higher slopes of the coastal mountain ranges. Some, like myself, are atmospheric amphibians—their homes sometimes below and sometimes above the top surface of the marine air. So, marked changes in weather and climate are found in short vertical distances. It is not unusual for me to leave for work in the morning in a balmy dry atmosphere only to encounter, quite abruptly, the cold damp marine air part way down the hill, just like a bucket of cold water in the face.

It's almost as if southern Californians had two oceans, the one they swim in during the summer and the other they drive around in most of the rest of the time. And this air ocean has an upper surface almost as well defined as that of the Pacific waters below. Consequently, it has a definite shoreline. I live on the shores of that upper ocean, 1000 feet above sea level. Just as the water's edge down at the beach oscillates back and forth with the waves and with the ebb and flow of the tides, so does the edge of the cool moist gaseous ocean surge back and forth from minute to minute, hour to hour, and day to day. Our house is like those rocks along a rugged coast that sometimes ride above the waves but at high tide disappear below the surface. The major point of difference is the magnitude of these changes in "sea level." Those of the Pacific are measured in terms of feet, those of the marine layer in terms of hundreds of feet (sometimes a thousand).

But we cannot stretch this analogy too far. The ocean of marine air does not everywhere have such a nicely defined shoreline. At its inland extremity the marine air has become so heated in its daytime travels over the hot land that it no longer differs much from the air above it. The interface between the two layers gets quite fuzzy and smeared out. No sharply defined interface exists any longer and, likewise, no well defined shoreline. So the marine air ocean is a strange ocean, one with a definite coastline in some places, where its upper surface is sharp, but in other areas with an upper surface too indistinct to form a coastline. In still another place it behaves in an even less ocean-like manner. Along the heated slopes of the mountains during the daytime this ocean gets so hot that it takes off uphill like hot air up a chimney. If the Pacific behaved this way our house long ago would have been washed uphill in a shallow flood of sea water.

Distinctions of distance inland and distance above sea level, however, do not completely characterize our local climate. Some of the routes the air takes on its journey inland are more susceptible to thermal insults than others. For example, the San Fernando Valley, 10 miles or so from the coast, has a climate like that of most areas about 30 miles inland. The difference: the air in reaching this area is forced to take a 20-mile detour (by virtue of stability) around the eastern end of the Santa Monica Mountains. It arrives at a point only 10 miles inland after suffering through 30 miles of heating from below. Motorists driving the short route up and over the mountains from the coast to the valley experience a sudden change in temperature at the crest as they pass from air with a short overland history to air with one about three times as long. So the pattern of climate and weather becomes all the more intricate.

Of course, there's more to local weather and climate than just the temperature and the humidity. There are the clouds and the rain, the sun and the shade, the sparkling clear air and the dreary atmosphere muddied with the aerial litter of modern civilization. These conditions also are very sensitive to the properties of Los Angeles' marine layer, particularly its ups and downs. This ocean of cool moist air normally surges up and down with a daily rhythm strongly reminiscent of the ocean tides. In most places over the Los Angeles basin the top of the marine layer changes in depth daily by as much as 500 feet. It's usually at its shallowest around sunset. During the night it gradually deepens. Then, just after sunrise, it starts to rise more rapidly and reaches its greatest depth sometime around midday. The afternoon is spent in a rapid shallowing, terminated by the sunset minimum. Its behavior is actually a little more complicated than this. There are variations from place to place. The peak depth is not reached simultaneously at all points in the basin. Rather, it occurs first at the coast, then at progressively later times at stations farther inland. In effect, the top of the marine layer has a moving bulge in it about 500 feet high. It starts at the beach an hour or two after sunrise and proceeds inland at 5 or 10 miles an hour, reaching the middle of the basin around noon. The cause of this moving wave is not completely understood, though it is thought to be a combination of the horizontal crowding and spreading of the air due to the waxing and waning of the sea-land breeze regime and the deepening of the marine layer by mixing and dilution with the warm air above.

One might think that a wave 500 feet high would be a frightening thing to behold. What a tourist attraction! But the Chamber of Commerce doesn't advertise it. You can't, after all, see it, not even when the top of the marine layer is sharply defined by the top of the stratus deck. The 500-foot bulge is spread out over a horizontal distance of something like 20 miles (say 100,000 feet) and has therefore a slope of approximately one in 200. Such gradual slopes defy detection by eye. Obviously it was not discovered by eye. Instead, it was detected with radiosondes, those automated upper-air observers that the Weather Bureau sends up on balloons to measure temperature, pressure, and humidity. Radiosonde records show the top of the marine layer as a marked sudden increase in temperature and decrease in humidity.

In World War II a network of radiosonde stations was established in the Los Angeles basin, under the direction of Professor Morris Neiburger of U.C.L.A., to study fog and stratus clouds. For the first time it was possible to compare coastal and inland stations simultaneously at time intervals as small as four hours. And so this interesting shape of the top of the marine layer was discovered. About a dozen years later, in conjunction with a study of the smog problem, we were able, using an instrumented aircraft, to make a closer examination of this interface between cool and hot air. By making aerial ascents and descents at all the local airports and noting the elevation at which the sudden change in temperature occurred it was possible to describe the three dimensional configuration of the marine layer in even more detail. Now we use such aircraft to examine the interior details of the layer as it is modified and ultimately destroyed by daytime heating. We can detect the thermals within the marine layer that are carrying the heat up from the surface, as well as the splashing at the top of the layer that mixes a little heat down. Gradually we are piecing together a picture of that short but eventful last day in the life of the marine layer.

In one respect, though, the local atmosphere is still hiding important secrets. They lie in the area of the horizontal squeezing and spreading (convergence and divergence) that periodically pile up or shallow out the marine layer. It is quite plausible that the development and decay of the usual sea breezes and land breezes and their inland counterparts, the valley and mountain breezes, are responsible. But we are not sure of the details. We don't observe the wind at the surface or aloft with sufficient precision and accuracy to be able to detect the rather small differences in wind that can produce the deepening and shallowing that are observed. We don't even observe the winds above the ground in the marine layer at enough different places to determine the pattern of winds there. Some new technological marvel will come to our rescue soon, we hope, one that will allow us to observe in the necessary detail the air motions that drive this daily pulsing up and down of the marine layer.

Now what have the marine layer's antics to do with clouds and precipitation? Just this: the marine layer is a prison of sorts in which is confined all the moisture that the air has picked up on its long tour across the Pacific. It protects this nearly saturated (sometimes completely saturated) air from dilution with its drier environment above. So long as the marine layer preserves its identity, so long does the prison remain intact, and so long is the possibility of cloud or fog formation preserved.

Let's examine the ways in which clouds form and dissipate in this ever-changing layer. The undulations up and down, the path inland, the daytime heating and nighttime cooling—all have an influence. Favoring the formation of cloud are the upward motions (cooling) that go with a deepening marine layer, and the nighttime cooling that comes with radiative losses from the top of the layer. The deepening that progresses during the night and through most of the morning is largely responsible for forming the clouds but, of course, is augmented by the nighttime losses of heat from the top of the marine layer. The usual clearing in the late morning or early afternoon is more the result of the sinking motions that go with the shallowing than of the heating that comes from the warm daytime ground surface, although this helps.

The stratus cloud, when fully formed, fills the upper part of the marine layer. Seen from below, it has the flat, untextured appearance of fog. Consequently the local inhabitants often refer to it as high fog. It blankets the coastal waters for hundreds of miles out to sea yet usually extends only a few tens of miles inland. The air farther inland has been warmed in its travel across the warm land on the daytime sea breeze and requires, therefore, more nighttime cooling before the dew point is reached. So, the farther inland you live the later the stratus will form over your house and the earlier it will dissipate. At a great enough distance inland it doesn't form at all. This selective behavior of the stratus cloud regarding distance inland serves to exaggerate even more the contrast in climate between the inland and coastal areas. Its very existence in mountainous areas near the coast produces the most dramatic contrast of all. The people in and below the stratus cloud deck live in a fuzzy gray world in the morning while their neighbors above, up on the ridges, live in a world full of sunshine made all the more brilliant by the reflection from the top of the dazzling white ocean of stratus.

Of course, there are infinite variations about this theme. No two stratus days are exactly alike. Sometimes the stratus comes in early (before sunset), sometimes late (around sunrise). Sometimes it burns off early (shortly after sunrise), sometimes late (well after noon). This variation is a source of considerable concern for the local weather forecasters. At times the stratus reaches all the way to the ground (then it's correctly called fog). Other days it is so high and deep that drizzle from it puts a hazardous slick layer on the freeways. These gross variations are imposed by changes in the large scale weather pattern. When cyclonic disturbances in the upper levels approach the southern California coast the whole area is subjected to converging air flow that squeezes the atmosphere, marine layer and all. This compression results in an overall, around-the-clock deepening of the marine layer and the formation of stratus so thick that it may not burn off all day long. The approach of anticyclonic patterns aloft has just the opposite effect, leading to overall shallowing of the marine layer and the complete disappearance of all the stratus for days at a time. The comings and goings of the stratus are involved inextricably with global as well as local weather disturbances.

So, much of Los Angeles' wide spectrum of weather can be understood in terms of the marine layer—its swelling and shrinking, its daytime heating, nighttime cooling, its systematic destruction by a hostile continent. And to its everlasting credit we must acknowledge the benign influence it diffuses during the twenty-four hours of its decline and demise. In that brief and final interlude it bestows on coastal California a moderate, pleasant climate in a place designated by global circulations to be a desert.

Chapter 11

SMOG, PRISONER OF
THE MARINE LAYER

Fog and stratus are not the only prisoners of the marine layer. Air pollution seems to be serving a life term. Without the marine layer Los Angeles has scarcely any smog. Every day of the year sees thousands of tons of pollution put into the Los Angeles atmosphere, yet at times Mount San Gorgonio, 80 or 90 miles inland, stands out bright and clear, as does Santa Catalina Island, 20 or 30 miles out in the Pacific. There is no pollution, no smog, anywhere in sight then, yet the factories are going full tilt and so are all the trucks, buses, and automobiles. The explanation is straightforward. On these delightful days there is no shallow marine layer over southern California. Instead, a deep air layer of little stability extends from the surface to 30,000 or 40,000 feet. Pollutants introduced at the bottom of such a layer are free to mix up to these great heights. Our aerial sewage is thinned out so completely that it almost disappears. The atmospheric prison has become so large, thirty or forty times the volume of the marine layer, that it is difficult to find the prisoners.

Now, Los Angeles is not the only city producing aerial wastes at rates of thousands of tons per day. If you live in any of the largest cities in the United States you participate in such a daily production. Yet none of these cities has a smog problem comparable to Los Angeles'. Why? The others usually are spared the shallow layer of ground air that imprisons all the pollutants emitted into it. Once in a while, when weather conditions give them low stable layers of their own next to the ground, they suffer too. But these occurrences are relatively rare.

It appears that the way to solve the smog problem, then, is to eliminate the marine layer. Obviously the depth of the layer severely limits the volume of air into which the pollutants can mix. If only that depth could be increased from 1000 to, say, 20,000 or 30,000 feet! But there is another way in which the volume of air is increased—by greater wind speeds across the city. If you compare two days having marine layers of identical depth but wind speeds different by a factor of two, the windier day will experience smog concentrations only one half as great as the other. On the favored day twice as much air will pass over the pollution sources. Consequently the daily output of pollutants is injected into twice the volume of air. It is fair to conclude that Los Angeles would be only half as smoggy if it were twice as windy. Unfortunately Los Angeles taken as a whole is not a windy city. The average wind speed is only about seven miles an hour, about the lowest for any location along the Pacific Coast.

So, the smog varies from day to day as the wind varies and also as the depth of the marine layer varies. Although Los Angeles lives in a marine layer three days out of four, it suffers severe smog attacks much less frequently than those figures might suggest. Often the winds are strong enough to prevent high concentrations of pollutants from accumulating, and much of the time the marine layer is deep enough to allow sufficient dilution to prevent a bad attack. But on those days when the marine layer is shallow and the winds very weak the insufficiently dilute fumes inundate the megalopolis. Angelenos, resignedly or bitterly, depending on their temperaments, endure the familiar eye irritation and the severely restricted visibility.

On such days the marine layer is an awesome thing

to behold, particularly from an aircraft. From below it has no form. One sees it as a fish must see the muddy water he swims in. But from above it is like looking down on a turbid sea. Hills rise above the layer like islands; the smog looks almost substantial enough to walk on. In our untainted freedom of the sky it seems incredible that we should be willing to take the plane back down into that murky air, to resume lives so unfavorably submerged. If you would discourage someone from settling in Los Angeles, make sure that he sees it first from the air and in the daytime. If you would encourage him, have him arrive by air after night has fallen. Sundown performs the ultimate in magic. Then the Los Angeles basin stretches out like a fairyland of lights, hundreds of square miles of them piercing the now barely perceptible smog.

It was natural that the airplane became the tool of the smog meteorologist. Using it as an observing platform, he could easily gain a proper perspective of the horizontal extent of the city's polluted wake. What's more, he could plumb its depths in many different places to fill out the picture in three dimensions. This sort of exploration is difficult on the ground where the lateral boundary is quite mixed up. Not so the upper boundary. It is sharp! As one rises up through the polluted air in a light aircraft he is first aware that he is nearing the top of the layer when the sky above begins to turn blue rapidly. He begins to see a fuzzy horizon encircling him, blue above, beige or brown below. He may think this is the top but it is not. He is still submerged. The horizon becomes less fuzzy. Then suddenly it is sharp and straight. He has risen out of the murky marine air and entered the desert above. Air in this new environment is bright and clear. Its lower boundary, though nothing more than polluted air, has almost the color of the solid desert and stretches away to the horizon farther and flatter than the smoothest desert dry lake bed. But when one looks directly down one can see through the dirty veil the ghost of the megalopolis below.

This flatness is in fact somewhat illusory. The temperature data from aircraft reveal that the top of the smog has the same sort of bumpiness that the top of stratus cloud has in the daytime, the result of the active thermal convection within the layer. But smog, even at its thickest, has rather tenuous edges. You can see through about 500 to 1000 feet of quite bad smog as compared to only 50 to 100 feet of stratus cloud. The individual bumps in the smog top are all but invisible. When sighting across the tops of the countless multitude of bumps between you and the distant mountains, you find them blending together to form a very flat and substantial looking plain. Really an incredible sight, one I never quite get used to.

Another characteristic of the air also changes abruptly here at this upper interface, the smell of the air. For reasons that I do not understand, I seldom detect a change upon rising out of the polluted layer but almost always am aware of it upon re-entering. Perhaps we who live in smog so much become accustomed to it, but shouldn't I notice the sudden absence? Well, my nose doesn't. But it does detect its sudden presence when descending back into the smog layer. It is interesting that the nature of the "fragrance" depends on where over the basin you make your entry. One particular place always smells like onions, another like dairy farms and still another like oil refineries. In all cases except possibly the onions the eyes confirm what the nose detects. An onion field seen from 1000 feet up could easily be mistaken for lilies, but smelled from the same altitude, it comes up onions every time. So the uniform appearance of the smog layer does not imply uniform composition.

We really do not know yet what it is that makes smog visible, but whatever it is it seems well distributed. The contamination doesn't seem to get airplanes dirty—usually, that is. Normally, planes fly through it only near airports on ascent or descent. The rest of the time they fly in the air above with its much better visibility. They spend little time actually in the polluted air. On one of our research flights, however, we did, inadvertently, pick up quite visible amounts of smog. It appeared as a thin dark, almost black, line deposited on the leading edges of the wings, the rudder, and the horizontal stabilizers, just where the surfaces of the plane impinge on the air at right angles. On this flight we were obliged to fly in the smog for over three hours while tracking balloons specially inflated to float within the dirty layer. Evidently the 400 or 500 miles flown through the smog while circling the balloon exposed us to enough of the particulate component of smog to provide this impressive accumulation. A rough computation indicated that about 10 million cubic feet of air came in contact with these thin blackened areas in the course of the flight, quite a substantial air sample.

The question is often asked, If the weather is responsible for the accumulation of air pollution, isn't there something that we can do about the weather to get rid of it? Can't we eliminate the marine layer somehow, or maybe increase the wind speed? At the present the answer is no. Many suggestions have been made. All have been considered carefully. Appropriate weather modification is still over the horizon, who knows how far away. Until then the weeping Angeleno is in no mood to wait. What's more I'm not sure that he would like the solution, even if we learned how to achieve it. For example, if we were to eliminate the marine layer by raising its temperature to that of the dry air directly above, the desert climate would indeed extend to the very beaches. For those who cherish the mild summer temperatures the cure might seem to be worse than the disease.

Even if we were able to increase the volume of air into which we dump our gaseous refuse to an acceptable amount, population growth and the attendant industrial growth might well accelerate the production of

aerial contaminants above the acceptable threshold
again within a score of years. Quite pertinently Neiburger has pointed out that we do not yet know what
maximum pollution input rate the atmosphere as a
whole can handle. For many years the marine layer
was spacious enough to handle Los Angeles' wastes. But
a time came, early in the 1940s, when it no longer
could. And now other cities, more favorably ventilated
than Los Angeles, are beginning to exceed the capacity
of their natural ventilation for the first time and are suffering smog attacks. As the rate at which pollution is
injected into the air continues to mount, more and more
cities will join the unhappy club. The prospects of
weather modification as the cure will diminish apace.
To continue our search only along the line of weather
modification would be analogous to solving the problem
of pollution of the Great Lakes and the Mississippi by
somehow moving ten times as much water through
them. If the problem must be attacked now, and it
must, we have to get at the pollution sources. And, of
course, this is what is being done in Los Angeles and
elsewhere.

When the search for the culprit in Los Angeles began back in the early forties, there were some obvious
candidates: those smoking chimneys in the industrial
districts and those smelly fumes from the refineries
and chemical plants, not to mention the municipally
operated city dumps as well as the neighbor's backyard
incinerator. I guess it's human nature to demand easy
solutions to our problems. The general opinion seemed
to be that there was a source (or at most only a few
sources) that were responsible for this new nuisance.
Find it (or them) and we would quickly and cleanly
rid ourselves of the scourge.

Aerial surveys supported what we already "knew."
The visible sources of smoke came from the industrial
areas. A dense network of wind stations was installed,
more than fifty in the area. Surface wind flow studies
often revealed that reported odors came from specific

sources of chemical fumes. In some cases of reported damage to house paint the meteorological finger pointed to plants where, sure enough, breakdowns in their processes had resulted in the inadvertent release of highly reactive fumes. So the meteorologist, turned successful sleuth, aided in the campaign. Improvements in smokestack design and industrial processes, combined with legislation and subsequent enforcement, all led to the virtual elimination of the visible sources and many of the odor sources. Nowadays when you fly over Los Angeles you see no smokestacks belching smoke even though there are more smokestacks than ever. You see no pall from city dumps, no myriad plumes from untold thousands of backyard incinerators. Unlike the smokestacks, the dumps and incinerators have been eliminated completely. But you do see smog. It comes from nowhere. It comes from everywhere. One gets the impression that it just oozes out of the ground. Obviously there are other sources that cannot be overlooked.

It was rather early in the game that attention was called to some less obvious sources of pollution. Much as one resisted the thought that cleaning up industrial, municipal, and backyard nuisances would not solve the problem, evidence of another multitude of suspects could not be disregarded. Surface wind studies frequently (not just once in a while) pointed the accusing finger almost at random about the municipal area. Careful studies of severe smog attacks sometimes indicated that the air came from industrial sections but as often showed that it couldn't have.

By this time, chemists had discovered that fumes given off in incomplete combustion, even though they might be quite invisible, could combine in the presence of solar radiation to produce eye irritation and reduce visibility in the ways characteristic of smog in high concentrations. So many of us had to face up—reluctantly, I'm sure—to the unpleasant prospect that the villains of Los Angeles smog would turn out to be not the easily pinpointed industrial sources alone but more than a million others too. These sources moved about the streets and freeways and, taken collectively, far outproduced the prodigious industrial complex (by a ratio of 4 to 1 in 1960).

So, my car and yours is as much the culprit. And the task of reducing smog takes on new dimensions. Realization that each of these millions of sources would have to be controlled individually was staggering, but the process of providing exhaust devices on vehicles already has begun. Still, a question remains. Will these devices reduce pollution input to acceptable levels? And if they do, how long will it be until the proliferation of industrial smokestacks and automobiles, so intimately tied to the population growth, raises the input of pollution over the smog threshold again.

There is a personal solution to the problem, of course. One can move to the desert. Or one might try moving to another part of town. There are great contrasts in smog from one part of town to another, just as there are changes in climate. The most favorable locations would be those either above the marine layer or upwind of the pollution source. Of course, the wind direction being variable, one cannot always be upwind without adopting a nomadic existence and moving as often as twice a day. Nor can you always be sure of getting above the smog. The daytime upslope flow on the sunny sides of the mountains frequently carries the smog right to the tops. I recently visited the astronomical observatory at Mount Wilson, almost 6000 feet high, that overlooks the entire Los Angeles basin. What it really overlooked that day was the smog. And I can't rightly use the word "overlooked" because I was in the smog, couldn't in fact see more than a mile or two through it. The daytime thermal upslope winds had pulled the smog, like a dirty rug, right up the southern slopes of the San Gabriels.

I was reminded of an occasion back in the 1930s when just the opposite conditions prevailed. While standing on top of Monrovia Peak, just 5 miles east of Mount Wilson and at slightly lower elevation, I was able to see the battleships at anchor in Long Beach Harbor some 30 miles away. In those pre-smog (and for me pre-meteorology) days what amazed me was not that the air was so clear but that battleships were so large. However, this sort of comparison is not fair. A clear view is still possible if one chooses the right kind of weather.

Before anyone sets out seriously to choose a smog-free home site in the Los Angeles area he should be advised that some of our worst smog attacks occur when the marine layer is completely absent! Yes, we have to consider that other 25 percent of the time too, our "unusual" weather. In one small part of this 25 percent of the time, air arrives at Los Angeles from the northeast quadrant, dry and warm, sweeping before it the last vestiges of the marine layer, and bringing the desert all the way to the beaches. When the winds are strong this weather bears a famous name, Santa Ana. But when the winds are weak it becomes—smog. It's our bad luck that in these circumstances Los Angeles is on the receiving end of another hot-air factory, similar to the one over the Pacific that concocts the marine layer. This one also is a large anticyclone, positioned over the Great Basin, that dry expanse of rough terrain between the Sierra and the Rockies. Again, sinking air spirals down and out of the system to produce a very stable layer near the ground, an inversion in temperature. This inversion usually is even lower than the one atop the marine layer, perhaps no more than 500 feet above the ground. Since there is no ocean in the Great Basin, the air beneath this inversion is very dry. So, on these occasions of weak wind from the northeast, Los Angeles gets hot dry smog.

On these days, beach communities smugly upwind of pollution sources most of the time find themselves downwind. The usually smog-free are now smog-bound. Ordinarily cooler, thanks to low elevation, than the inland communities, they become the hottest spots in the entire area—10 or 15 degrees hotter than the deserts. This perverse sort of weather can be experienced in any season except, strangely enough, the summer season. Even in dead of winter the temperature may soar up into the nineties for a day or so, and the smog alerts are readied. It is more usual, however, because it typically is very windy, for this hot weather to be beautifully clear. On such days Los Angeles' output of more than 10,000 tons of pollution is swept right out to sea on the Santa Ana winds. Los Angeles basks on its coastal plain under a bright winter sky. No tawny blanket of smog fuzzes its outlines, only a few streaks of wind-blown dust and sand downwind of the passes.

The mountains increase markedly Los Angeles' chances of getting smog in these hot dry spells. The area of weakened winds in the lee of the San Gabriels, often referred to as their wind shadow, becomes relatively stagnant when the winds abate, and pollutants tend to accumulate. It is interesting how the mountains switch their role from hero to villain, and not always easy to tell just which role is being played. Consider, as an example, the accumulation and dispersal of smog in the marine layer. Do the mountains act more as a dam against the movement of the cool smoggy marine air, or do their heated daytime slopes provide chimneys through which to vent the smog from the area? The answer depends on the time of day and the distance inland of the mountains. At night all mountain ranges act as dams to the marine layer. During the day their influence as dams is less and less the farther inland you go. Much careful research remains to be done on the effects of local terrain before answers to such questions can be given with any confidence. (Fig. 13)

We conclude that smog is an unholy alliance between a substantially constant daily dose of aerial contaminants and a highly variable amount of natural ventilation. It is the weather that calls the tune, smog or no smog, because it is the weather that specifies just how much natural ventilation there will be—how rapidly the air will move across the sources of pollution, how

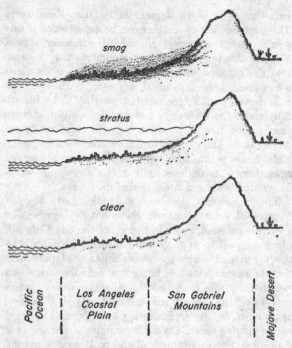

FIG. 13. *The barrier of the San Gabriel Mountains to the east is both villain and hero in the tear-jerking drama of Los Angeles' infamous smog.*

far up into the atmosphere the pollutants will be able to mix and dilute. But over the years it is the character of our local weather, changeable as it is from day to day and month to month, that is least changeable. It is the daily dose of pollutants that is likely to change, and for the worse. The solution of the air-pollution problem can't wait for weather control. The timetable is too uncertain. Somehow the amount of aerial sewage dumped into our atmosphere must be reduced, and this in the face of population increase and in increasing trend toward urbanization.

Chapter 12

WILDFIRE AND THE SANTA ANA

Smog is just one of the disasters visited upon mankind. For this affliction man must accept a share of the responsibility even though, as we have pointed out, local atmospheric conditions are the central influence. But there is a great variety of natural disasters to which, in one way or another, the atmosphere and its disturbances contribute directly. Fires, floods and famine, avalanches and landslides, hurricanes, tornadoes and blizzards, lightning and hail are all weather-connected. You could perhaps add to the list localized torments I haven't mentioned that are inflicted upon your own part of the world.

If one were to let oneself be swayed unduly by the benign climate of southern California, one might conclude that it should be a place relatively free of weather-connected disasters. But actually it has its fair share. I consider smog to be a natural disaster of sorts, and its very existence depends on the benign nature of the climate. There are others that depend on Los Angeles' more violent weather—the floods, the fires, the landslides. Floods are more and more becoming a thing of the past for this area, but not because we have learned to control the weather. What we have learned to control is the water after it has reached the ground, with dams and channels and a labyrinth of underground drains. As for landslides, they, like smog, are often as much the product of man's activity as of the atmosphere's. Man irresponsibly scrapes and cuts the earth's surface, most grievously in hilly terrain, and winter rains then provide the lubrication for the landslides. Here too we may expect much improvement, not by stopping the rains (we need those), but by more intelligent behavior on our part.

Fire, unlike floods, landslides, even smog, is still largely beyond our ability to control. This startles you? Well, perhaps I should qualify that remark a little. Once fire has started under "fire weather" conditions on the chaparral-covered slopes of southern California's mountains, there is only dim hope of stopping its scourge. We can heartily endorse the campaign to be careful with matches, even suggest that people give up smoking if they are not already convinced of its adverse medical implications, but some fires still will be started by such natural causes as lightning. And while fervently supporting the "careful" campaign, reason suggests the inevitability of inadvertent ignition in the presence of an ever-increasing population crowded up against the fuel (dry chaparral) on the slopes of the surrounding mountains.

Fires will be started, and if the weather is "right" they will turn into conflagrations lasting for days and consuming not only chaparral and trees but houses and automobiles as well. Needless to say, lives can and have been lost. But surely, you say, our technology must be catching up with the problem. Maybe so, but the gains are hard to detect. It is the nature of some problems to yield slowly. Maybe this is one of them. Certainly in my lifetime the big fires in the mountains have shown no disposition to cease or even to taper off. The same old firebreaks that made hiking the ridges so much easier than crashing through the buckthorn and sage are still maintained, as are the fire roads. New roads and breaks have been added, and new techniques of fire fighting, such as borate bombing and fire jumping. But every year or two we are "treated" to the same spectacle: the hills aflame, and sometimes residential neighborhoods with them. Sometimes it is the slopes of the San Gabriels, sometimes the Hollywood Hills or Topanga Canyon in the Santa Monica Mountains or the slopes above Malibu.

If we had the know-how to control the weather, we would have all we need to stop the holocaust. These disasters always occur in the same setting, the Santa Ana wind. This dry hot wind from the northeast and north sucks the moisture out of the chaparral to set the stage. Then after the unfortunate spark ignites that first dry blade of grass or tiny twig, the strong winds quickly fan it to forest-fire proportions. The fire is rapidly carried by the winds to the brush immediately downwind. Furthermore, bits of burning brush are lofted high in the air on extremely buoyant updrafts over the fire, updrafts so violent that they sometimes form whirling tornadoes of flame. The embers get caught in the even stronger upper winds and may fall to earth miles ahead of the main fire to start new spot fires. Small wonder that a modern well-equipped fire-fighting force, combining the facilities of the city, county, and U. S. Forestry Service, could not prevent the loss of over 450 houses in the famous Bel Air-Brentwood fire of November 1961. The fire fighters, with the aid of borate bombers and the latest techniques, were able to save many homes, and miraculously no life was lost. But the fire stopped only when the Santa Ana stopped.

What an eccentric performer is the Santa Ana. On some occasions it endears itself to Angelenos by sweeping the basin clean of smog or by bringing summer-like relief to a winter cold snap. On others it visits the worst sort of disaster, lives lost, homes lost. But most of the time for most of the people it counts as beautiful weather that carries along only minor nuisances—leaves and twigs blown about, maybe a little more dust about the house.

Using the same fine surface wind network that was established by the Los Angeles Air Pollution Control District, it is possible to examine in some detail the fascinating face of the Santa Ana as it appears over the Los Angeles basin. If there is one thing that typifies the Santa Ana for Angelenos it is the grand rush of the air to the sea. But close inspection of the data reveals remarkable deviations about this general flow pattern— sea breezes completely counter to the general flow and big whirls or eddies 10 or 15 miles across. All things considered, a rather chaotic if grand rush to the sea, with considerable dissent here and there and from time to time.

The seat of this confusion is the San Gabriel Mountains that stand over a mile high and 50 miles long between the basin and the source of the winds. Behind this formidable wind screen lie the city and its outlying communities, not feeling the full brunt of the wind but suffering from the buffeting that goes on in its wind shadow. This shadow has depth as well as width and length. It is a volume that extends in general from the lee slopes of the mountains all the way to the sea, but its shape and size vary a great deal from one situation to the next, even from one hour to the next. Sometimes it is rather deep, perhaps reaching almost to the ridge tops of the San Gabriels. Other times it is shallow, so shallow that the strong northerlies sweep all the way down the lee slopes of the mountains and a mile or so out into the plain or valley floors before rebounding again up over the troubled air in the wind shadow. So, sure enough, the grand rush to the sea takes place. But it generally goes over the top of Los Angeles and around both sides, leaving the city in a pocket of freakish winds, not unlike the crazy burble of air that follows a speeding truck or train. Those of you who have ridden in the back of an open truck know well the mischievous gusts and swirls that play havoc with any loose debris.

Perhaps the biggest surprise in the wind data is the inevitable afternoon sea breeze observed somewhere or other in the basin, even on the days of strongest Santa Ana. We looked at six years of data and found not a single exception. To be sure, it is a pale imitation of the usual marine-layer type of sea breeze, averages only 4 or 5 miles per hour and normally lasts but a few hours in the afternoon. But it is there, blowing right in the face of the formidable Santa Ana. Sometimes, though not usually, it covers the entire basin except for the areas under the jets of strong winds around each end of the San Gabriels. More usually the sea breeze occupies a corridor 10 or 20 miles wide from the western beaches to the slopes of the San Gabriels, the result of admirable teamwork between the thermal contrasts produced by the bright sunshine at the coastline and at the base of the south-facing slopes of the mountains. This is an impressive demonstration of the power of thermally produced local circulations. But one must be mindful of the San Gabriel Mountains that made it all possible by removing the teeth from the gale.

I can see the frown of disbelief on the faces of those of you who have lived in the Los Angeles area. As a native, I can sympathize and wonder with you. We all know the Santa Ana as that hot dry gusty wind that rips the branches off trees, sometimes pulls whole trees down. No sea breeze comes around in the afternoon to give a little relief from the bone-dry furnace-like air. What's wrong with these wind data? Well, it's something hidden in the data that makes for this confusion between the wind records and our recollections. The winds plotted on the maps are in the prevailing (most frequently observed) wind direction, and the average wind speed is given over a time interval of one hour. Such maps were made for each hour of the day. Now what we remember about the winds during those few hours in the afternoon when the maps of prevailing winds spelled out sea breeze were those strong but infrequent gusts that tugged at the treetops every once in a while. What we don't remember (probably didn't even notice) is that gradual drift of air, maybe 4 miles per hour, that prevailed in between the gusts.

Perhaps the most reasonable picture is that of the

raging Santa Ana omnipresent above our heads, a strong wind that roughs up the top of a shallow sea-breeze layer in which we are submerged. Occasionally a big gust comes along from above that sweeps out a hole in this shallow layer and there the trees suddenly feel the full brunt of the Santa Ana, but only briefly. The rest of the time it is quiet down among the buildings, trees, and assorted small obstacles that camouflage effectively the 4- or 5-miles-per-hour drift from the sea. Yes, but why is it so hot and dry? What kind of sea breeze is this? Well, it is nothing more than air which passed us by some time ago, maybe overhead, maybe not. Now after a brief swing out to sea it has been caught in the turbulent swirl of the San Gabriel's wind shadow and revisits us as a sea breeze, little moistened or cooled, by its brief interlude at sea, and even warmed a little by its slow journey over a sunny landscape.

While I am shoring up my defenses against my neighbors, who also know the Santa Ana from long experience, I must mention the great variability in wind behavior according to position with respect to the San Gabriels, the passes around either end and the steep canyons that crease its southern slopes. Some really wild variations in wind behavior occur in areas downwind of the passes and canyons. Strong jets downwind of the passes waggle back and forth, turning the desert blast on and off on an erratic schedule. To people caught in these jets the Santa Ana can be a real terror. Consider the motorist who drives through the dust and sand picked up downwind of the passes. For him the visibility may suddenly drop to near zero as he enters the cloud of driving sand and dust. Gusts nearing hurricane force (75 miles per hour) rock his car. The visibility is so bad he may even lose sight of the hood of his car. If he does succeed in coming to a halt before hitting anything, his car may receive a sandblasting that leaves the windshield so badly pitted that it will have to be replaced.

So the Santa Ana means different things to different

people. It's a nervous time for those of us who live up in the chaparral. It's an uncomfortable time for those who live downwind of the passes, certainly a difficult time for the housewife there who must contend with the dust and sand all over the place. It can be a miserable time for millions in the Los Angeles basin if smog gets into the act during its decline. But most of the time for most of us it is a beautiful few days when our rather extravagant environment of ocean, wide plain, and high mountains lies brilliantly exposed to eyes all too accustomed to haze, smog, and stratus.

Chapter 13

FOGS, FROSTS, AND FREEZES

In completing a list of the local weather phenomena that contribute to local disasters one can include the fogs, frosts, and freezes. The last two affect primarily the vegetation and the pocketbook. As for the first, a certain number of lives are lost each year to accidents in which dense fog is a causal factor. Despite aids to navigation—ancient (lighthouses and foghorns) or modern (radar and loran)—a certain number of ships collide in the fogbound harbors or go aground on rocky points along the coast. And once in a while an air crash is attributed to fogging-in of an airport, but, thanks to modern technology, the hazard of fog has been reduced greatly.

Fog does not engender the fear and panic that fires and earthquakes can. We live rather comfortably with it. For me it has a pleasant nostalgia. I like waking up to the mysterious gray world of fog. It reminds me of many pleasant things—like the school bus that my dad drove, creeping along rural roads, feeling for the next corner and its cluster of school children. But lately our Los Angeles fogs have developed a rather frightening aspect. The freeways have become the setting for chain-reaction multiple auto collisions. Motorists accustomed to racing at 65 miles per hour along with hordes of others on their way to and from work sometimes do not reduce speed sufficiently in foggy conditions. By the time they see the obstacle ahead it is already too late, and one car after another piles up. More than one hundred cars have collided in a single such accident on the freeways of Los Angeles. Perhaps the benevolence with which some of us view fog will give way to a measure of apprehension, at least until we can depend upon some intelligent accommodation of driving habits to the hazard of low visibility.

There are several different types of fog. Some of it arrives here after having formed elsewhere. The meteorologists call this advection fog. Most of it forms right here on the spot. It can have different names depending upon how it forms. In fact one of two things happens to air to cause fog to form: either (1) it may be cooled down until its temperature equals its dew point, or (2) water vapor may be added to it until its dew point rises up to and equals its temperature. Anyone who has steamed up a cold bathroom by taking a long hot shower has himself manufactured a fog of the latter type. He has not cooled the air to form fog; rather, he has evaporated water vapor into it (increased its dew point) until it was saturated. If you have seen "steam" rising from a pond on a cold winter morning you will appreciate why it sometimes is called steam fog. The most striking examples of this occur in the Arctic, when subfreezing air drains out over open water. Such fog bears a poetic label, arctic sea smoke. I need not add that we do not see it here in southern California. But we do see its cousin, the wispy mist that rises above the surface of heated backyard swimming pools on cold winter mornings.

Most of our fog is of the other type, that which takes the air as is and cools it down. The typical chain of events starts with the very commonplace flooding of the Los Angeles basin with marine air. But it must be an uncommonly shallow layer so the cooling will be concentrated on as small a mass of air as possible. This condition allows the maximum temperature drop for a given amount of cooling. Typically it would happen in the winter when the nights are long and the cooling

takes place over the maximum length of time. Furthermore it takes a night on which the skies are clear. Under such conditions the moist marine air loses its heat
by radiation to the sky—no blanket of clouds above to
intercept its radiation and radiate energy back. Finally
it must be a calm night so that the shallow layer of
cooled air next to the ground remains intact, does not
get mixed up into the warmer air aloft. Given these
conditions, we get fog that goes by the remarkably simple title of radiation fog. Perhaps you have seen it as
the low-lying mist that hangs in the low spots on crisp
windless winter dawns.

Such radiation fogs come in all shapes and sizes, as
dictated by the terrain. The chilled air drains down
and accumulates in the low areas—a remarkable imitation of the behavior of water except that it moves much
more slowly. The fog forms everything from small
ponds to great inland seas. Every winter brings a lake
of radiation fog several hundred miles long to the great
central valley of California. This valley, a combination
of the San Joaquin and Sacramento valleys, is surrounded completely by mountain ranges and runs about
half the length of the state. It has the High Sierra on
the east, the Tehachapis on the south, the Siskiyous on
the north, and the coastal ranges on the west, with only
the narrow Golden Gate as a chink in the wall. Often
winter storms leave behind a shallow layer of clear,
cold, moist air in this vast valley. Not infrequently the
following anticyclone settles for a while over the western United States, providing the valley with dry, cloudless, relatively warm air aloft for weeks at a time. The
perfect prescription for a radiation fog of staggering dimensions. And the great central valley gets it! It's best
seen on pictures taken by meteorological satellite. Once
the fog forms, each night reinforces it with additional
cooling that more than compensates for the small
amount of daytime heating. Weeks may pass during
which the sun is not seen. The fog is destroyed only

when a storm arrives and applies the big broom, with turbulent winds sweeping the length of the valley.

Of course, this fog, like most fogs, is really the result of both the cooling and moistening of the air. On passage of a winter storm the landscape is left soaked with rain, and a certain amount of subsequent evaporation helps to saturate the air next to the ground. But sometimes neither the cooling nor the addition of vapor is enough to saturate the air. Then, under the same conditions of no wind and no cloud and cold winter air, the stage is set for another sort of local weather problem, frost. Under such conditions anywhere over land the temperature continues to fall all night long as a result of the radiation losses from the ground. If they reach the freezing point we get frost.

For most of us frost is certainly no catastrophe, for a special few it can be as disastrous as flood or drought. We are thinking, of course, of the farmers and ranchers who grow crops that cannot tolerate subfreezing temperatures. Southern California's agriculture is of types extremely susceptible to freezing. Citrus orchards and vegetable farms are prime examples. The farmers can protect themselves in a variety of ways. The first, when possible, is to plant crops on land that is not down in the hollows. Next, the farmers must practice weather modification. This may sound a bit formidable, but let me remind you that you have been practicing weather modification as long as you have been wearing clothes, living in houses, and sleeping under blankets.

The citrus grower's more or less standard technique to increase the temperature of this shallow layer of subfreezing air is to burn oil in smudge pots that are spotted about in the orchards. A great deal of preparation is required, and a lot of hard uncomfortable night work. It also is expensive. So this weather modification is avoided when possible. Much depends upon a good temperature forecast. The U. S. Weather Bureau has a special fruit-frost forecasting center that puts out radio bulletins every winter evening for the benefit of the ranchers. The special audience listens with a rapt devotion unparalleled among the most avid soap opera fans.

Sometimes these frost periods persist for so many days that fuel supplies run low. This crisis can lead to fairly desperate search for things to burn. I remember once many years ago when the pall of smoke over our house from the orchard heaters was so dense that the sun at midday was just a dull red disk in a strange dark sky. Of course, this shielding compounded the difficulty for the next night because the ground received very little heat from the sun on that day. It stayed cold all day long. No wonder the smoke was darker than usual that day; for lack of anything else to burn some ranchers had set old automobile tires afire in the orchards. I know of no recent occurrence of this sort. Now the pall from orchard heaters is held to a minimum, in conformity with law, by use of very efficient heaters.

It is interesting to note that at least one other method is used to heat the air around the trees. It is the stirring of the air with large fans mounted on towers that rise above the crowns of the trees. The idea is not to move the air horizontally but to stir it up and mix warm air from above the trees down into the cold air below. The method is effective when the layer of cold air is shallow. But there are those nights when, no matter what precautions are taken, the crop will be lost. This doesn't happen every year, of course; otherwise there would be no citrus orchards or vegetable farms. But it does happen often enough to remind us that weather modification has its limitations.

On such nights we have what is known as a freeze (as opposed to frost). It's a very different weather situation in one very important respect. It is windy and the air is already cold through a deep layer. A near-freezing torrent of air that had its beginnings in the Canadian Arctic on the other side of the Rockies pours across southern California. With the additional nocturnal radiative cooling of the earth's surface, the temperature of this air plummets maybe 10 degrees F below freezing. The fans do no good. There is no layer of warmer air just above the treetops to be stirred down. Besides, plenty of stirring goes on already in this rushing torrent of air from the Arctic. As for the orchard heaters, it's as if someone opened all the doors and windows. What little heating is achieved is swept right out the window.

As I approach the end of this book about local weather, seen from the perhaps biased but surely sophisticated viewpoint of an Angeleno, I look out the window at eucalyptus trees whipping back and forth in a blustery rainstorm. There is the splatter of sheets of water blown off the flat roof onto the patio. The air is too full of mist and rain for me to see chaparral 100 feet down the slope. We are above the base of a vast rain cloud blanketing southern California today. A midwinter storm has arrived from the Northwest. Yesterday and the day before Washington and Oregon were lashed by gales and drenched with heavy rains. Snow has piled up on the Cascades and the Sierra. Now the storm has reached us. With only a few days left of Christmas vacation, there's a good chance that some of our students, off at the mountain ski resorts, will be snowed in, may miss a day or two of school. Our rain gauge here indicates that 2.7 inches of rain already have fallen, though the rain started only twelve hours ago. This is not typical, but neither is it unusual. We get storms like this every year or so. Because our house is 1000 feet up the south-facing slopes of the mountains and the winds are coming from the south, the clouds get extra lift here and give us more rain than dwellers on the coastal plain are getting. So even the effects of this large cyclone, which is anything but local in dimension, are shaped to some extent by the local terrain.

Local maps of rainfall distribution (isohyetal maps) reveal the effects as marked differences in precipitation between the mountain slopes and the coastal plains and valleys, the higher mountains getting several times as much precipitation as do the plains. But this is only the average condition. Depending upon the direction of the general flow of the rain-bearing layers, their stability or instability, and other complications, the local rainfall can take on a wide variety of patterns. Some storms actually bring more rain to the low flat areas than to the mountains.

If this storm behaves in typical fashion the westerlies, by late this afternoon or tomorrow morning, will have carried the center of the cyclone well inland, and we will find ourselves in the northwesterly flow around the back side of this big atmospheric swirl. The character of the precipitation and the type of cloud will have changed, as will the visibility and the temperature. And these remarkable changes, unlike those we have been talking about in this book, will have been dictated by other than local effects. Instead, they will follow a timetable set down by the global circulations. This cyclone, which is about as big as the western United States, moves according to the grand flow pattern that spans oceans and continents, even hemispheres, the general circulation of the atmosphere. Local effects will not deserve credit for that first big crack in the heavens that I expect here late this afternoon, or for that shift in the wind to the northwest and the sudden substitution of a panoramic view of Santa Monica Bay for the present fuzzy view of a few rain-lashed eucalyptus trees on the slope below.

So, as this discussion of Los Angeles' local weather comes to a close, the weather outside is behaving in a very unlocal way. What is happening is the result of global geography and global wind circulations, terrain features, the size and dimension of whole oceans and whole continents. Mountain systems the size of the Rockies make their presence felt. But the little coastal range that I sit upon at this moment does no more than rearrange the pattern of rainfall a little bit and put a few burbles in the surface wind pattern. Inappropriate as it is that the weather should behave this way at a time when I would like to stress the powerful influence of local terrain on weather, it is a useful reminder that sometimes these local effects take a back seat. In some places, indeed, maybe yours too, they may take a back seat most of the time. But whichever it is, they will leave their marks (conspicuous or subtle) on the face of the weather about you. Take a look. The marks are there.

Chapter 14

A METEOROLOGY FIELD TRIP

Meteorology, like geology, botany, zoology, and many other sciences, involves exploration in the field. Herein lies much of the pleasure associated with these pursuits. Although the professional meteorologist may use global observational networks, artificial earth satellites, instrumented balloons, airplanes and rockets in his field work, there is much discovery left for the amateur—particularly in the more restricted field of local meteorology. Using no equipment beyond his own eyes, ears, nose, and sense of touch, he can enjoy that special exhilaration that comes with discovery. He can get along even without thermometer, rain gauge, or wind vane.

Perhaps you've never heard of a meteorological field trip, but you've heard of a geological field trip. We have the advantage there of the geologist. He cannot sit still and expect the rocks to come to him. Even in situations where they might, avalanches for example, it is not a recommended procedure. So the geologist moves about through his rocky environment with an observant eye and an abundance of natural curiosity about the earth and the way it got that way. While a lot can be learned about the atmosphere and its behavior by sitting still and letting the weather come to you, even more can be learned by moving through it. I wish you could fly around in it in a small airplane or sailplane. Those of you who have sailboats already have an excellent platform from which to learn something about local weather, especially local winds. But so do those of us who every once in a while take trips in automobiles. Some of my most memorable local weather jaunts have been on foot or by bicycle.

Since no special equipment or gear is required, you can make every trip you take a meteorology field trip regardless of its primary purpose. Weather-watching does not require your total attention and concentration. If you are on a vacation trip, you will still be able to enjoy the scenery. Only now the clouds will have more than just aesthetic significance. That cold wind down the canyon will be something more than invigorating or uncomfortable. I think you will find that meteorology complements nicely geology, botany, zoology, and the other scientific disciplines that can bring so much added pleasure and meaning to a vacation trip into the wilds.

Your meteorological excursion need not, of course, be a vacation trip. For me it is often the 5-mile drive to school or a journey somewhere in connection with my work. As an example of the sorts of weather specimens you can turn up on an 8-hour meteorological field exercise, consider the following one-day auto trip home from a scientific meeting.

It was one of those days when there wasn't a cloud for 500 miles. A large high-pressure area (anticyclone) had taken possession of the Great Basin. The high had remained stationary for several days. Hot dry air manufactured in the vast subsiding motion of this stationary anticyclone inundated all California. This air from the continent had replaced the customary brisk winds from the North Pacific. The whole state was suffering from a heat wave. Temperatures reached 100 in some parts of the Los Angeles basin. Even cool San Francisco reported an 89. Though it was October 24, the weather along the California coast was hotter than it had been at any time the previous summer.

The usual temperature distribution, coolest at the coast and warmer inland, was reversed exactly. The hottest air was the air which had descended farthest, had been compressed the most. And that, of course, was the air at sea level. It had started many thousands of feet higher and some 20 degrees F cooler above the Great Basin. It had come to the shoreline by way of a curved descending path. The temperature had risen one degree C for each 100 meters of the descent (5½ degrees F for each 1000 feet). On this day the coolest air in the western United States was to be found over the inland areas. The day before I had been near Reno, Nevada, (over a mile high) and had traveled to the Monterey Bay region (sea level), south of San Francisco. No thermometer was needed to detect the marked warming.

Now it was eight in the morning, and we started south by car along the spectacular Big Sur coast. For almost 100 miles U.S. Highway 1 is but a notch carved into the seemingly perpendicular western slopes of the Santa Lucia range. These coastal mountains, several thousand feet in height, are softly rounded and gentle in appearance near the crest, with expansive meadows interspersed with dense forest. But this rounding down from the heights continues to steepen until, at about 1000 feet above sea level, the slope becomes almost vertical. From there on down the Santa Lucias form a 1000-foot sea wall, slanting at an alarming angle into the sea. Across the face of this wall runs a scar, U.S. Highway 1. In some places the surgeon seems to have done an admirable job, a clean sharp incision. In others landslides have wiped out long vertical wedges of sage, toyon, sumac, and the other shrubby vegetation that elsewhere softens the aspect of the awesome precipice. Every few miles narrow canyons perpendicular to the coast cleave the mountains. In these canyons stand the southernmost groves of the great coast redwoods of California. Here the highway dips down almost to sea level only to rise again to spectacular heights, perhaps 1000 feet, on the face of the steep broad promontories between canyons. So the road goes up and down and in and out with nothing to the west except empty space and nothing below except the sea.

Usually it is a wild and lonesome scene. Brisk damp Pacific winds drive the breakers against the rocks. The meeting of sea and land is a chaos of foam and fury. Explosions of spray drench the cliffs. But today it is a different ocean, one more suited to its name, Pacific. In the absence of the vigorous northwesterly winds, the ocean is a mirror for the cloudless sky. Only a gentle swell, like wavy imperfections in a pane of glass, features an otherwise featureless expanse. Today, where the road rides high on the face of a promontory one does not hear a distant roar below. Nowhere, high or low, does one feel the cool damp assault of a clammy ocean wind. Instead, the air is clear, still and warm. What a departure from the typical situation! This remarkable transformation, this total change of mood is due in its entirety to the change of only one ingredient in the Big Sur recipe, the wind. The cliffs, the trees, the canyons, the water, the giant kelp, the sea lions on the rocks, the gulls and cormorants—all are here. Only the wind has changed. But it is the catalyst that fashions of the usually wild and invigorating Big Sur coast a scene of unusual languor and serenity.

The reason? Today the precipice where the Santa Lucia Mountains meet the sea is downwind, an unfamiliar situation for the Big Sur area. The ocean, thus shielded by the mountains from the assault of the easterly winds, lies unperturbed except for the swell generated by forgotten winds that tugged at the sea maybe a thousand miles out in the Pacific several days ago. The strong dry winds from the continent pass undetected above our head. But they are there. The evidence is unmistakable. Some distance off shore a few patches of ruffled water deface the glassy expanse where the wind out of the east briefly brushes the surface, then mysteriously rises again.

I stop to watch these wind patches, while eating breakfast in the camper, to see whether they are changing. In particular, there are strange meandering streaks of calm water that thread their way through the roughened water. Are these streaks persistent? Fifteen minutes of watching reveal that the patterns do change shape fairly rapidly, but the calm streaks tend to persist. Oceanographers have explained that these smooth streaks in otherwise wind-roughened water are due to collections of small floating material in the sea surface that tends, like oil, to prevent the formation of ripples. I notice, however, that as the roughness of the patch of water increases, apparently with an increase in the strength of the wind, the slick streaks begin to roughen up too and disappear. This watching of the patches of roughened water becomes a pastime with me on this day, practiced for over 200 miles of California's mountainous coastline, abandoned only as I leave the coast at Ventura, not far from Los Angeles. But it isn't the only distraction, as if one needs distractions from the vistas furnished along this spectacular coast. I soon become aware of abrupt changes in air temperature.

Sometimes for a short distance the air becomes cooler, only to assume its previous warm dry nature again. I put my hand out the window as a thermometer and wait for another change in temperature. Sure enough, another one comes along. And as with the first it happens where the road curves in through another deep narrow canyon. It must be a drainage wind off the mountains. The still-shaded west-facing slopes of the Santa Lucias hold the night's chill. They are so steep that the sun will not touch them for several more hours.

So I dangle my hand out the window for an indicating thermometer and play the game of forecasting the cool spots along U.S. Highway 1. Every time the road heads back toward a narrow stand of redwoods marking another narrow canyon in the face of the precipice, I expect momentarily to feel the splash of cooler air on my hand—and I am never disappointed. With such sparse and imprecise observations the mind conjures up a picture of the atmosphere here in the lee of the Santa Lucias, a mass of nearly stagnant warm air huddled in the shelter of the precipice. Above it warm easterlies, deflected up and over the mountains, slant down toward the glassy ocean; except for a few burbles that dig down and make the capricious wind spots on the surface some distance off shore, it is miles downwind where the easterlies finally reach the water. Right next to the mountain, cooled by a nighttime's loss of radiant heat to a cloudless sky, a shallow skin of cooled air runs in rivulets off the broad rounded promontories into the narrow canyons and threads its way through the towering redwoods to the sea. So each canyon has its invisible cataract of cold clear air.

With this simple picture of the situation I was able to make fairly good forecasts of the temperature changes before I encountered them. Very satisfying! But suddenly my confidence is shaken. I run into cool air where I shouldn't, out on the face of the cliff, a little away from a canyon. At first I stubbornly refuse to change my ideas, write it off as a freak of some sort. When it recurs, however, not once but several times, I reluctantly accept the fact that my model of the local atmosphere is oversimplified. There's something else going on here that I haven't considered. Isn't it odd that we should be so reluctant to accept information that contradicts our current beliefs when it is just such information that refines our first guesses and takes them another step nearer the truth?

The hand out the car window is not enough instrumentation for this dilemma. I stop the car in the cool air at the next canyon and decide to hike down to the seashore to make a vertical temperature sounding. It had gradually dawned on me that it might be as much the ups and downs of Highway 1 as its ins and outs that had produced the sharp changes in temperature. As well as ducking horizontally in and out of rivers of cold air coming down the steep canyons, maybe I also had been bobbing up and down out of the top of a cool lake of marine air that lay above the Pacific and splashed lazily against the cliffs. After all, the road descended as it went into the canyons and ascended as it went out, so that either explanation would suffice. Certainly the surface of the Pacific was a first-class site for cooling warm dry air. The surface water is in the low 60s F this time of year, 30 degrees F colder than this air from the continent on this exceptionally hot day.

The canyon where I stop is Vicente Creek, one of the smaller ones. A concrete bridge about 100 feet high spans it. I scramble down the canyon wall, already in cool air, alert for any abrupt temperature changes and any air motion that might have a bearing on the dilemma. It is there! The cool air suddenly becomes distinctly colder at about 50 feet above sea level, and a gentle breeze, about 3 miles per hour, carries this colder air down the canyon gorge toward the coast. I am entering the drainage air off the Santa Lucias, a river of cold air submerged in an ocean of cool marine air. Not 20 yards from the beach I am stopped by a narrowing of the canyon to a small gorge, complete with waterfall and pool below. A delight to both ear and eye! The polished vertical walls of the gorge prevent me from swimming my way through. Though I could drop down into the water, I would need a ladder or a rope to get back out. What a disappointment. It would have been a nice adventure. I hike back out in the face of the cold air current drifting down the canyon. Again at about the 50-foot level, just under the bridge, the wind stops as I emerge from the cold-air river into the cool motionless air ocean, just as a few minutes later and about a mile up the road the car would emerge from the cool-air ocean into the hot dry air of California's heat wave of late October 1965.

So the picture is refined. Apparently a cool puddle of air covers the Pacific. This air, formerly hot and dry, has been cooled by contact with the cold ocean and fed by rivers of even colder air chilled by contact with the nighttime slopes of the mountains. This layer (we'll call it a marine layer) is a few hundred feet thick. U.S. Highway 1 dips in and out of this layer as it takes its frequent excursions back down into the narrow canyons. The top of the layer is not absolutely flat, but shows undulations such as those we have seen on top of fog. So sometimes after rising above the marine layer as we left the canyon we would find ourselves again reentering in a large swell at the top of this invisible ocean. Well, now I feel better; the observational data are falling back into place. But I leave my hand out the window not only to continue my forecasting game, but in the expectation that new clues may lie ahead to paint in more details on this portrait of the invisible air. I am not to be disappointed.

As we move farther south along U.S. Highway 1 two important things change: the geography and the time of the day. Both have effects on the sea of air through which the car moves. I stop at Limekiln Creek to make another temperature and wind sounding. This time I am able to get all the way down to the water's edge. It is a wider canyon than Vicente Creek. But the answers are the same. Two cold layers beneath a warm one, the lowest of which moves down the canyon. And now the lowest layer is beginning to be detectable by eye as well as by feel, particularly when the car is high on a promontory and one can see miles of the rugged coast stretching out to the south. A faint whitish haze fills the lowest layer of the atmosphere just along the shore near the mouths of the canyons. Its sharply defined top traces out its own shoreline about 50 feet up the side of the cliffs. Below, the gentle swell slaps against the rocks, throwing enough spray in the air to provide the basic ingredients, tiny salt particles, for its telltale haze. It isn't Big Sur's usual extravagant display of surf and spray but it is enough to mark our lowest cold layer of air with natural sea haze.

Often my mind wanders from problems atmospheric. There is so much that is pleasant and distracting about

this coast. Then a sudden splash of cold air on my hand
out of the window brings me back to meteorology. I
quickly take stock of our location and, sure enough,
there we are passing a small canyon. I begin to realize
that I am by good fortune taking the ideal field trip
for the amateur meteorologist. I begin giving the atmosphere the same attention that a geologist must give a
rocky landscape. I begin to anticipate. What will happen when the sun finally starts to warm the steep cliff?
The upper warm dry winds—will they surface along the
coast near San Simeon where a plain several miles
wide separates the Santa Lucias from the shore? To be
sure, before my trip is over a sea breeze does develop
in some places in response to the heating of the land.
In others the landward retreat of the mountains allows
the hot dry winds from the continent to scour out the
shallow marine layer and rough up the water all the
way in to the beaches.

I am first aware of the changing time of day when
my hand feels a sudden warming. My first reaction is
to interpret the sudden warmth as a change in air temperature. But my hand has suddenly "seen" the sun.
Like most thermometers, it assumes a temperature well
above that of the air when exposed to solar radiation.
A quick survey of the local scene and I discover my
error. The rays of the sun now slant across the face of
the precipice, catching just the tops of the tallest sage,
sumac, and toyon.

Now the car is approaching the southern end of the
Santa Lucias. Just ahead a coastal plain that intercedes
between ocean and mountains comes into view. Will
the beach now be far enough downwind of the mountain obstacle to feel the hot dry breath of the northeasterlies? The answer is obvious, even before the car
descends to the plain. The low hazy layer of air that
had been banked up against the cliffs at about the 50-
foot level is still there. Now it spills over the low cliffs
that form the western boundary of the coastal plain. I
can see where a tongue of it crosses the road several

miles ahead. There's no northeaster blowing there. The
air is drifting in from just the opposite direction, from
the sea. And corroborating that finding is the still glassy
ocean.

The character of the road changes abruptly as it descends to the plain. It undulates gently up and down
over a grass-covered expanse several miles wide. Cattle
graze on both sides of the road. Standing on the crest
of one of the rounded peaks, 4 miles to the east, is
William Randolph Hearst's castle, Casa Grande. At its
elevation it must be bathed in the warm dry winds.
Suddenly as we descend into a creek bed the car enters
the hazy sea air. A strong odor of the sea assails my
nostrils. Simultaneously the temperature drops. I stop
the car a little beyond the lighthouse at Point Piedras
Blancas to check the wind. Whatever wind there is, is
too weak to feel; I toss a little straw in the air and an
ever-so-gentle sea breeze is discovered. The several
hours of heating of the coastal plain have done their
job—the sea breeze begins.

The gentle undulation of the road brings the car in
and out of the cool pungent sea air, and when the
road wanders inland the air gradually loses its chill. A
half mile inland, over the sun-warmed earth, it is a
warm sea breeze already. My eyes leave the road
more than they should in a search for wind indicators.
The only ones I can find are the bent heads of the wild
oats along the roadside and the smoke from one backyard incinerator near the little coastal town of Cambria
Pines. They all indicate a very weak sea breeze. Now
the road leaves the plain as we head up a little valley
and the sea disappears behind a small coastal range.
It gets hot and the weak sea breeze disappears, to be
replaced by an equally weak southeasterly. I puzzle
about the origin of such a wind, but come up with no
answer. Now that's a little more like the atmosphere
I'm accustomed to—one generously spotted with question marks, little pieces of the great puzzle that don't

fit yet but which will, we trust, when we get enough
other pieces put in place.

After a hot 15 miles out of sight, sound, and smell
of the sea we suddenly emerge from the confinement
of the coastal hills and behold before us again the ocean.
But here it is an ocean feeling the full force of hot
dry winds from the continent. No glassy wind shadow.
Eucalyptus trees lean in the wind, their boughs trailing
off toward the sea. Spindrift rises up in beautiful arches
over the backs of the breaking waves. The strong northeasterlies have found a chink in the mountain defenses
here in the vicinity of Morro Bay and scour out a
wide swath in the marine layer. The hot breath of the
wind from the interior is felt right on the beaches. No
damp sea haze here.

Caught up in the excitement of the sudden change
of scene, I stop the car and hike the few hundred yards
across dry grassland to view at close range the wonders
wrought by strong winds directly in the face of breaking waves. I stand on a 15- or 20-foot bluff, my shirt
flattened against my back by the hot dry wind, and
look down on a narrow beach of rounded rocks and
pebbles. No sand. The water shoreward of the breakers
sloshes up and down in unpredictable patterns along
an irregular cliff. The scene is too refreshing to be resisted. I descend the cliff and go for a swim—the high-
light of a trip full of highlights. Water in the low 60s
pushing and shoving, swirling rocks and pebbles about
my legs. Air in the low 90s, dry as a bone, a perfect
complement to the chilling surf. What wonders the
weather has conjured up. A swim in this frigid surf on
a more usual late October day would be pure torture.
The equally frigid ocean wind would only, as the saying
goes, add insult to injury. I clamber out of the water.
No need for a towel. The hot blast dries me off in
minutes. And I am on my way again.

The winds from the continent sweep down the gentle
rolling slopes behind Morro Bay and completely fill the
bay. Spray from the breakers along the 5- or 6-mile

stretch of curved beach is skimmed off and swept seaward. At Cayucos a completely asymmetrical Monterey cypress, its branches trained by decades of strong sea breezes to extend horizontally from the trunk only in the inland direction, is being tossed and tousled by a contrary wind. It is reminiscent of a bird standing with its tail to the wind, feathers all awry.

The coastal area along Morro Bay is the only place along the highway where we actually encounter the strong dry winds, except for a very short piece of coast to be traversed later near Santa Barbara. Everywhere else the wind shadow prevails. Now that the sun is high, weak sea breezes are the rule along the immediate coast. Where the road ventures inland more than a mile or so the sea breeze gives way to chaotic puffs of wind first from one direction, then from another, sure evidence of thermal convection dispersing the feeble marine layer. The highway plays hide-and-seek with the ocean for the next hour or so, shuttling us back and forth between cool sea breeze and warm convectively stirred air until finally the car tops Gaviota Pass and moves down the southern slopes of the Santa Ynez Mountains, California's longest stretch of east-west coastline. From here on the highway follows the coast closely; we will be constantly near a source of cool marine air. Whether or not we receive its benefits depends upon the winds here in the lee of another mountain range about as high as the Santa Lucias but not quite as steep.

As we descend the pass the Santa Barbara Channel lies before us. The Channel Islands, some forty miles off shore, appear through a faint dusty veil, have the look of desert mountains. And why not? The intervening atmosphere is mostly desert air with its light burden of finely divided soil. The sea is like glass except, again, for the isolated wind patches off shore. It is almost a carbon copy of the situation we saw along the Big Sur coast, but there are two very important differences:

(1) now it is afternoon, and (2) here on the narrow coastal plain the road never rises more than 100 feet or so above sea level. At this time of day the drainage winds, born of nighttime cooling, have long since been destroyed by daytime heating. We should be on the alert for their opposite number, the sea breeze. Whatever wind there is is too weak to be detected from a moving car.

At Refugio Beach we are surprised. A roughened patch of sea surface extends all the way to the shore. The eucalyptus trees are swaying toward the sea and the air suddenly becomes hot and dry. We've entered a jet of hot air from the continent. But it is quite narrow. Only a mile down the road we re-enter cool marine air, just where the roughened sea surface terminates. The air in the wind shadow is almost motionless, but here and there a fairly brisk sea breeze is encountered. At El Capitan Beach the boughs of the trees trail inland, and the air abruptly turns quite cool. This unusually cool air was rubbing against the cold Pacific only a few minutes ago, the length of time it takes air moving with a brisk sea breeze to negotiate the few hundred yards from the waterline to the highway.

So our last stretch of coastline on the journey down to Los Angeles provides us quite a variety—sea breezes, near calms, and one good hot blast from the continent. It's been quite a satisfactory meteorological field trip, if an unplanned one. I make my last stop at the beach on the Santa Barbara campus of the University of California for another refreshing swim. This time I have the company of hundreds of students, some on surfboards, others soaking up sun on the beach while trying to study. I wonder how many of them are aware that they are spending this exceptionally hot October Sunday afternoon right in the middle of a meteorological laboratory. Not many, probably. One needs "special eyes" to see the invisible atmosphere. Now it's time for you to try yours.

INDEX